COMBAT AND SURVIVAL

WHAT IT TAKES TO FIGHT AND WIN

VOLUME
2

Originally published in the United Kingdom in weekly parts **COMBAT & SURVIVAL** is a study of the armed forces at work. It shows the skills taught to soldiers and the way in which military units operate. It examines the weapons and equipment used by different armies; and, by looking at recruit training and exercises, **COMBAT & SURVIVAL** demonstrates how the armed forces develop individual responsibility, leadership and initiative.

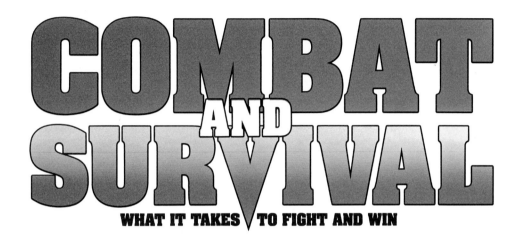

COMBAT AND SURVIVAL

WHAT IT TAKES TO FIGHT AND WIN

VOLUME
2

H. S. STUTTMAN INC. *Publishers*   Westport, Connecticut 06880

Contents

Volume 2

Published by H. S. STUTTMAN INC.
Westport, Connecticut 06889
© Aerospace Publishing 1991
ISBN 0-87475-560-3

SECURING THE LANDING ZONE

By the time he'd struggled to get the equipment out on to the ground he was glad he'd been able to get the car so close to the Drop Zone. And God help those three if they'd brought more than the bare minimum of kit – they'd bloody well have to carry it themselves! He kept on looking up at the low grey racing clouds as he put the reflective panels into their frames and arranged them into the letter of the day. An L: L for Larry. It was his name. A good omen? He hoped so.

He hated these minimum personnel drops. He'd not only have to mark the whole DZ himself, but charge around picking everything up afterwards, too. And no security team. He loosened the Colt Centennial Airweight in the shoulder holster for the twentieth time, and then settled down to wait for the reassuring drone of the low-flying aircraft, and the parachutes lowering in the early morning sky....

Marking drop zones

Even if his navigation is excellent and his instruments spot-on, the pilot should still be helped in the final stages of the approach by signals from the ground. At night these can be made by electric torches, flares, small fires or vehicle headlights.

In daylight, the best DZ marking method is the square panels that are supplied as sets to Special Forces units. If they're not available, use bed-sheets or strips of coloured cloth, but make sure they stand out against the background. The squares or strips are used to make up distinctive shapes or letters which are changed every day according to the unit's Standard Operating Instructions.

Smoke grenades or simple smudge pots of burning oil aid identification considerably.

Radio homing devices become more and more popular as the technology that supports them improves, but remember that they need to emit a radio signal to operate. Any signal that you can pick up, the enemy can pick up too.

Ground release points

The ground party has a much better chance of computing the Wind Drift Factor (the distance that bundles and personnel will be carried by the wind) than the pilot does, so they allow for it when marking the Ground Release Point.

The wind doesn't start to act on the load immediately it leaves the air-

REPORTING DROP ZONES

The minimum amount of information required to establish a Drop Zone comprises the following:

1. Code Name and type of DZ – primary, secondary or water.
2. Location and map grid co-ordinates.
3. Open quadrants measured from the centre of the DZ and reported clockwise from the north.
4. Course for incoming aircraft, measured from the centre of the DZ.
5. Obstacles within the reporting radius.
6. Reference point, such as a landmark that can be identified by name alone on issue maps.
7. Special instructions.

Leaping into the blue on exercise: Special Forces parachuting techniques are used to deliver combat teams and military equipment to secret locations deep in hostile territory. Special Forces units stand ready to organise guerrilla armies behind the lines, forcing the enemy to divert forces from the front line to guard installations and strategic roads and railways.

Altitude and temperature
Remember that at high altitudes and high temperatures the density of the air is sharply reduced. This means the helicopter cannot carry as much cargo and will need a longer distance to take off and land.

Approach path
Helicopters need at least one approach path 75 metres wide. For a night landing a helicopter requires a minimum space 90 metres in diameter.

Weapons storage
While you are inside the helicopter and strapped in, hold your rifle with the muzzle pointed to the floor so that, if you accidentally fire your weapon, the bullet goes through the floor and not up towards the vital parts of the aircraft.

Secure camouflage
You should remove all the local vegetation, bits of scrim etc that you are using as personal camouflage when you are entering or exiting the helicopter. Loose bits of camouflage can be sucked into the air intakes and do serious damage to the helicopter.

Fast Attack Vehicle
This armed off the road racer has an excellent cross-country performance and enables Special Forces teams to operate over a much larger area. Weighing just over half a tonne, it can be armed with a Chain Gun, a .50-cal machine-gun or a TOW anti-tank missile launcher.

Avoid the jetwash
When exiting a CH-47 Chinook you must keep going in a straight line after you hit the ground. If you turn to either side you will be caught in the ferocious jetwash from its engines. This is hot enough to set fire to your personal equipment!

craft. The rule of thumb is that the load will travel in the same direction as the aircraft for around a hundred metres before starting to slip off to the side.

Drift is calculated by a simple formula: aircraft height in feet times wind velocity in knots times a constant – three for bundles, four for personnel.

Release Point Markers can then be offset according to the likely wind drift. Obstacles along the flight path might prevent the pilot from seeing

Vital cargo can be dropped without landing with a technique known as Low Level Parachute Extraction Resupply System (LOLEX). The aircraft flies a couple of metres above the ground and a parachute fitted to the cargo pulls it out of the rear door.

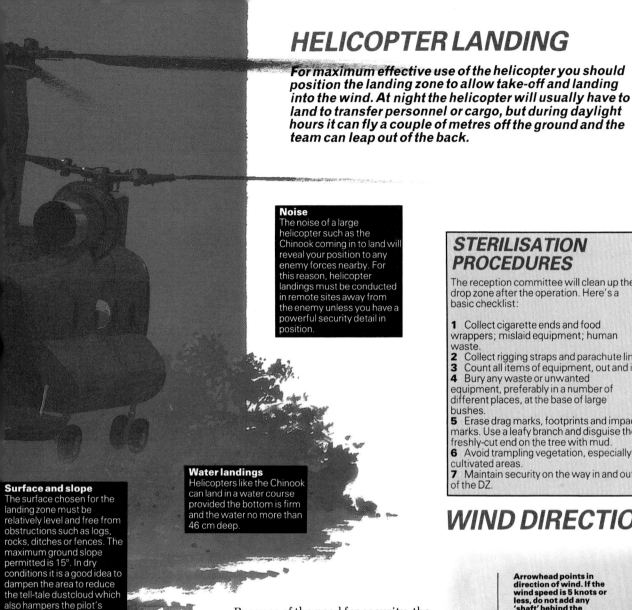

HELICOPTER LANDING

For maximum effective use of the helicopter you should position the landing zone to allow take-off and landing into the wind. At night the helicopter will usually have to land to transfer personnel or cargo, but during daylight hours it can fly a couple of metres off the ground and the team can leap out of the back.

Noise
The noise of a large helicopter such as the Chinook coming in to land will reveal your position to any enemy forces nearby. For this reason, helicopter landings must be conducted in remote sites away from the enemy unless you have a powerful security detail in position.

Surface and slope
The surface chosen for the landing zone must be relatively level and free from obstructions such as logs, rocks, ditches or fences. The maximum ground slope permitted is 15°. In dry conditions it is a good idea to dampen the area to reduce the tell-tale dustcloud which also hampers the pilot's visibility.

Water landings
Helicopters like the Chinook can land in a water course provided the bottom is firm and the water no more than 46 cm deep.

STERILISATION PROCEDURES

The reception committee will clean up the drop zone after the operation. Here's a basic checklist:

1 Collect cigarette ends and food wrappers; mislaid equipment; human waste.
2 Collect rigging straps and parachute line.
3 Count all items of equipment, out and in.
4 Bury any waste or unwanted equipment, preferably in a number of different places, at the base of large bushes.
5 Erase drag marks, footprints and impact marks. Use a leafy branch and disguise the freshly-cut end on the tree with mud.
6 Avoid trampling vegetation, especially in cultivated areas.
7 Maintain security on the way in and out of the DZ.

he markers, and to reduce this possibility there must be a clearance on the ground of 15 metres for every metre of the aircraft's height above ground. An obstacle 30 metres high mustn't be closer than 450 metres from the ground markings.

Markers should be sited in such a way as to be visible only from the direction from which the aircraft is approaching. This may mean screening them on three sides, placing them in pits with the appropriate side sloping, or, in the case of panels, mounting them at an angle of 45 degrees.

Unmarked drop zones

In particularly sensitive operations, it may be necessary to make deliveries of personnel and equipment to unmarked drop zones. This usually means a daylight or full-moon drop into a zone that has a particularly well marked geographical feature to identify it.

Because of the need for security, the ground party will have no way of communicating with the aircrew. The pilot will have to calculate wind drift for himself, using the latest available weather reports as a guide, and make allowances accordingly.

Electronic homing devices should be used whenever possible to help the aircrew recognise the DZ, but very careful arrangements are necessary to keep transmissions to a bare minimum.

High Altitude Low Opening

Precision skydiving, an increasingly popular sport, grew out of a Special Forces infiltration technique known as HALO - High Altitude Low Opening – parachute infiltration. Dropping from around 10,000 metres, the parachutists fall free, controlling their direction with hand and arm movements that act in the same way as the control surfaces of an aircraft.

DZ markings indicate the landing point itself in this technique, because the parachutist is able to make correc-

WIND DIRECTION

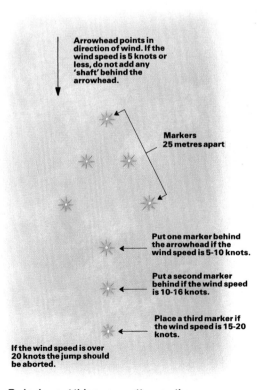

Arrowhead points in direction of wind. If the wind speed is 5 knots or less, do not add any 'shaft' behind the arrowhead.

Markers 25 metres apart

Put one marker behind the arrowhead if the wind speed is 5-10 knots.

Put a second marker behind if the wind speed is 10-16 knots.

Place a third marker if the wind speed is 15-20 knots.

If the wind speed is over 20 knots the jump should be aborted.

By laying out this arrow pattern on the ground you tell the pilot and parachutists the direction and strength of the wind, which enables them to judge the timing of the jump.

tions for windage. In the last few hundred metres of the descent, however, he will be subject to the same forces that act during a normal descent, and so it is necessary to show wind speed and direction by arranging the target marker in the shape of an arrow pointing into the wind. Up to five knots of wind are indicated by an arrow head, adding one additional marker, to form a tail, for every further five knots of wind speed.

Using sophisticated electronics, it is not necessary for the target area to be visible from the aircraft, so the HALO jump can be made from above cloud or at night. Equipment can be free fall jumped too, using altimeter-triggered or timed parachute release and the same aiming techniques used in high altitude precision bombing.

The ultimate headbanger! A member of US Special Forces free-falls from 8,000 metres with a Claymore mine strapped to his helmet.

The reception committee

The reception committee is split into five parts, but a single person may, of course, take on more than one role. The five functions are
1 Command party, to control and coordinate the operation and provide medical support.
2 Marking party, which sets out and collects markers and assists in recovering equipment and personnel and sterilizing the site.
3 Security party, which ensures that unfriendly elements don't interfere in the operation.
4 Recovery party, ideally two men for each bundle or parachute. They should be spread out along the drop axis at the same interval as the drops are expected. Any back-up should be stationed at the far end of the drop track, because the drop is more likely to overshoot than undershoot. The recovery party is also responsible for the clean-up 'sanitisation' of the drop site, and that includes briefing all members of the reception committee on proper procedures. A surveillance team should keep watch over the DZ for 48 hours after the operation to warn of enemy activity.
5 Transportation party, responsible for getting personnel and equipment away from the DZ according to a prearranged system. The transportation party will usually include all members of the command, marking and recovery parties.

Security

Because security and concealment is so important to Special Forces operations, you must pay a lot of attention to those considerations when selecting reception zones. Three factors are important: freedom from enemy interference on the ground; accessibility by means of concealed or secure routes for the reception committee; and proximity to areas suitable for hiding supplies and equipment.

Avoiding the enemy

It goes almost without saying that the aircraft's route into and out of the DZ must avoid enemy troop installations. There must be a very high level of patrol activity around the DZ for some time before the operation is due to take place. When the aircraft is actually scheduled to land, rather than merely drop a consignment from the air, vehicles with mounted automatic weapons should be available, to keep pace with the aircraft on both sides during landing and take-off (bear in mind that the vehicles will have to be moving and up to speed at the point where the aircraft will touch down.) If oncoming fire is received the crews of these vehicles must be in a position to suppress it immediately.

USING REFERENCE POINTS

OBSTACLE: radio mast

042° 6 km

DROP ZONE

159° 8 km

REFERENCE POINT: lake

Help the aircraft find your drop zone by providing reference points with three digit bearings and distances measured from the centre of the Drop Zone. Dangerous obstacles like radio masts or high hills should also be reported in the same way.

C-130 Hercules equipped with a skyhook for covert operations; the yoke used to guide the lift line to the centre is folded back. Inside the aircraft is an electric or hydraulic winch to haul up the man or cargo.

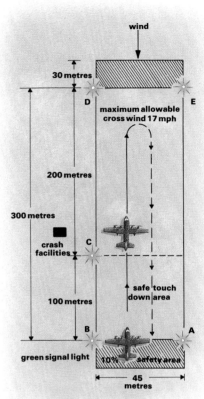

Above: Minimum dimensions of a night landing zone for light aircraft. The area at the side for crash facilities is not essential, but it is worth clearing if you have the time and space.

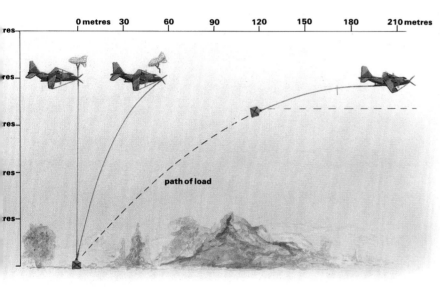

Skyhook is used to extract a single person or small package by aircraft without the plane having to land. Gas bottles inflate the balloon with helium and attach the other end of the line to a harness fitted to you or the cargo. The aircraft's yoke catches the line and snatches the person or cargo into the air.

Aircraft are actually brought in to land only if there's no other way to complete the mission, and that usually means when people or equipment are to be evacuated. Purpose-built light aircraft are able to land and take off in very short spaces, but their range is extremely limited.

In general, medium aircraft need a flat, cleared space 1,000 metres long and 30 metres wide. Even light aircraft need 350 metres to land and take off in safety. 'Flat and cleared' in this context means no ditches, ruts, logs, fences, hedges, bushes or rocks bigger than a man's fist – quite an undertaking! It's clear from this that constructing a landing strip will be a major operation, and one that won't be undertaken for just a single mission.

There are field expedients, though – ice, for example. Twenty cm of ice will support a light aircraft, and 60 cm of ice – quite common enough in high latitudes – will take the weight of a medium sized transport plane. Wide, sandy beaches can also be used without further preparation. The stretch of sand between high and low water marks is usually firm and even.

Skyhooks

One of the most dramatic of all Special Forces airborne operations is the skyhook – a method of picking up passengers and cargo without touching down. Put simply, skyhook operations require an aircraft fitted with a yoke - a horizontal 8-metre wide fork – on the nose, and an 18 cubic metre helium-filled balloon fitted with 150 metres of lifting line.

The skyhook kit, in two containers, is dropped to evacuees – wounded US personnel, downed aircrew, guides, even corpses where it is politically advisable to recover them. It consists of the balloon and two containers of gas to inflate it, lifting line, protective clothing and a harness. An amphibious version also includes an inflatable boat.

The skyhook kit is dropped on the first pass over the DZ. The person to be extracted puts on the suit and harness, attaches the lift line and inflates the balloon. As it rises, he sits facing the approaching aircraft and composes himself. On the aircraft's second pass it catches up the lift line, releases the balloon, and the evacuee is hauled up into the aircraft.

Combat Report

Vietnam:
Long Binh Patrol Part 1

In May 1969 Mike Glendon, serving with the 5th Royal Australian Regiment, took part in a two-week patrol while on operations around Long Binh and Bien Hoa, leaving from a Battalion Fire Support Base.

Sergeant Godfrey's bellowing voice rang out early one afternoon, calling the platoon for a briefing in the skippers' area. You could hear the moans and groans; we knew another patrol was coming up, and we all hated moving in that bloody heat.

The good news was that we didn't have to move out until the next morning. The bad news was that it was a recon patrol. We had to patrol 24 hours ahead pf D Company into an area containing a known Viet Cong camp. Apparently the VC had been hitting American patrols and attacking ARVN outposts. Our job was to find the camp, bring D Company in, and join them to clear it out. We were told to pack more than the usual ammo, which gave us the willies.

I didn't get much sleep that night as the drop shorts (artillery) were busy on H&I (Harassment and interdiction) missions. I checked my pack and ammo and rifle again before breakfast – not that I felt like eating anything.

Rough going

Then there was the usual hanging around: we had to run about like blue-arsed flies getting ready for the APCs that were to take us out for the first two klicks, then they were late. Anyway, we eventually set off, but the APCs found it rough going; also it was very noisy and we felt vulnerable. The VC must have been able to hear us for miles.

A couple of hours later we were on our own. Our section was lead party, with me and Trevor as scouts. So far, the going was pretty good.

By 11.30 I was knackered. We'd been going for nearly four hours and the skipper had given us a 10-minute smoko, although we didn't feel much like smoking in that heat: it felt like someone was drawing the breath out of us. It was so tempting to drink our water bottles dry. It took a lot of willpower to take just small sips. At least we weren't lead section now, so the going might be a little easier.

Bad news came at 13.00 when the skipper

said we'd gone too far off our compass bearing and would have to cut back. The problem was, there was a bloody great ridge in the way, so we had to go up. It took over four hours: it wasn't that high, but it was bloody dense and slippery from the previous day's rain, and we were struggling with loads of 40 kg on our backs. If the VC had hit us then, our casualties would have been bad.

Then we hooched up for the night. First we dug rough, shallow fox-holes, just in case Charlie hit; then we cleaned our rifles, put Claymore mines out, and ate. At 19.00 we had a stand-to, and my watch duty was from midnight until 02.00 – a horrible time. By midnight you've just dropped off, and after 2 you can't get back to sleep again.

Another stand-to at 05.00. It had been a quiet night; one of the lads thought he heard Charlie moving, but it was probably only an animal.

Where were the VC?

By 06.00 we were saddling up to move out when we heard Vietnamese voices: they just walked on by. The skipper sent a section to find out who they were, but they lost them. They did find a well-used track, though, which we decided to follow as it ran more or less in the same direction as our compass bearing. Only one problem: if the track was well-used, that meant that Charlie was around too.

Three hours later we had seen plenty of VC tracks but no contact. In the primary jungle the going was still not too bad, and the tree canopy stopped the sun from roasting us alive. But the humidity still got to us.

In late morning we came across what we thought was a VC outpost. It proved to be old and unused, but we still had to take care while searching the area. We learned our lesson a long time ago about booby traps: you don't trust anything, no matter how innocent it looks. Everyone was uptight. We knew the VC were around; we could see signs of them; and we had heard them. We knew it was only a matter of time before we hit them or they hit us.

At 14.00 we had a smoko and changed lead sections, and hadn't gone far when the lead scout completely vanished. We found him at the bottom of an unfinished well, looking very shaken and white. He'd thought he'd fallen into a man-trap. He was bloody lucky: it could have been a punji-pit. If it had, he'd have been dead.

About 01.00 Charlie hit us

That afternoon was the worst so far. The jungle had become secondary and the going was bloody hard. Also it had started pouring down with rain. It was a waste of time trying to stay dry; all you could do was put up with it. The noise it made was horrendous, which meant the VC couldn't hear us, but it also meant we couldn't hear them. We stopped for the night, which was obviously going to be a damp one with no sleep.

At 18.45 we stood to. We were all soaked. The only good thing was that my watch was 04.00 to 06.00, which at least meant the chance of some shut-eye.

But at about 01.00 Charlie hit us. We thought there were only about four of them; they opened up on us every now and again trying to get us to return fire and give ourselves away. We stayed quiet, but had to stand to for more

The long patrolling operations depended on regular resupply by helicopter. As the days went by we found many signs of VC presence but made no full-scale contact with the enemy.

An officer from the 5th Royal Australian Regiment arranges a helicopter pick-up.

than an hour. For the rest of the night we could hear the VC moving about.

By morning they seemed to have moved off and the skippers decided to move us away for about half a klick. We were to stop and have some chow, but no fires. We had been following the track but keeping well off it. We knew it had become a cat and mouse game: it wasn't doing our nerves any good, but it was certainly keeping us alert.

At about 09.00 one of the guys, Hans, got hit by a sniper, in the chest. We hit the ground and waited to see if we could spot the sniper, but of course we couldn't. Our section had to sweep through the area to look for him. The Dust-Off (casualty chopper) took Hans away late in the morning. We thought he might make it if he got to hospital in time, but he was making a horrible gurgling sound and red froth was coming out of his mouth, and he was crying. We were all feeling down, and bloody angry.

The leeches were worse than ever

A couple of hours later we were back on scout duty. We hadn't gone very far when I came across some Vietnamese huts. For about three minutes I really thought we were in trouble, but then after a check I realised they were very old and no-one had lived in them for months. But there were still plenty of signs of the VC around the track, and those signs were new.

That afternoon it rained again. We were due for a resupply the next day; good news as it might mean clean socks and mail. The bad news was that it would put the weight of our packs back up to the original 40 kg. The night was very quiet but the leeches were bad.

The next day I was still on scout duty. We had to get to our resupply drop-off point by 11.00, and the rain was turning everything into a swamp. The going was getting really hard and slow, and the leeches were worse than ever.

The chopper brought in our resupply about 11.30 and we heard the bad news that Hans had died. We split up our rations and ammo in a black cloud of anger and hurt. God help the VC if they hit us now. The rain started again, and the skipper told us we could hooch up early for the night. I think he realised the mood we were in.

The next six days were the hardest of the patrol. We saw signs of the VC and at night we heard them, but we never made contact. The rain got worse, and so did the humidity. We had stopped thinking about Hans: we hadn't forgotten him but we couldn't afford to let ourselves get too emotional or we would have gone crazy.

On the 20th the fun started.

Continued on page 76

STRIKE FROM THE SEA

A moonless night, a deserted stretch of coastline. A periscope breaks the surface of the silent sea for a moment, sweeps round once, then disappears beneath the waves again. A lone swimmer, dressed in black from head to foot, emerges from the surf and creeps up the beach, buries his equipment and disappears into the trees. Another US Special Forces operation is under way, and the enemy doesn't know the first thing about it.

Special Forces operations often start and finish on a beach. Even though airborne insertion is faster and more flexible, when safety and secrecy are the first considerations the unit commander will often opt to go in by submarine, landing his men from inflatable boats or getting them to swim. This is how US Special Forces set about landing men and equipment from the sea.

Submarines are self-contained, safe from prying eyes. This means that amphibious Special Forces missions can be mounted at extremely long range – from the other side of the world if necessary. The long journey time can often be an advantage in itself, because it allows the operational plan to be studied, pulled apart and put back together again until it is foolproof.

The first consideration is the type of boat available to carry the team to the landing site. Where security comes first, this will usually be a submarine, but that will put a severe limitation on the amount of equipment that can be carried, which may mean that a resupply mission will be necessary. However, for infiltrating small groups of people into existing operations, or for mounting raids, the submarine is ideal.

The team leader's first job is to familiarise himself with the characteristics of the vessel assigned to the operation. Amongst other things this will determine how the team's equipment is to be packed, because everything must be in secure waterproof bundles.

The US Navy SEALs are the equivalent of the SBS and specialize in clandestine operations along enemy-held coastlines. Coming ashore from submarines or special assault craft, they recce ahead of amphibious assaults or take out targets from shore-based missile sites to enemy ships in harbour.

6 points for leaving a surfaced submarine

1. Crew members and troops should be fully briefed on the debarkation plan.
2. Inspect all your kit before the debarkation.
3. Wait for the crew to man their debarkation stations first before going to yours.
4. Swimmers debark in pairs from the conning tower of the submarine, which will surface with its decks awash.
5. Form up in the control room with all your kit. If there is space the first pair can be in the conning tower ready for the submarine to surface.
6. If possible, rehearse the whole debarkation procedure before you do it in a tactical situation.

Space is very limited in submarines, but there is room in the flooding compartments for kit such as inflatable boats, and that's where they are carried.

The mission can be split down into four stages.

1 Movement to the disembarkation point. This part of the operation is normally under the control and charge of regular navy personnel.

2 Transfer from the ocean-going vessel to the landing craft, and movement to the landing site.

Left: Submarine enable you to approach close enemy coast wit being detected a reduce the amou time you spend on the water.

Underwater infiltration

As radar and anti-aircraft weapons become increasingly effective, underwater infiltration has become an increasingly important method of infiltrating Special Forces troops. The key to any successful infiltration may be summed up as Short, Simple and Secure. Underwater operations using SCUBA equipment provide an extremely secure method of infiltrating short distances by water.

Shallow depth
Try to make your approach at the shallowest possible depth so that your air supplies last longer, and you and your equipment do not suffer the problems associated with sustained diving at great depths. There is another reason: swimmer detection systems find it harder to detect people at shallow depths.

Facemask
You can test whether a facemask fits you properly in two ways: (**1**) Hold it gently in place with one hand, inhale through the nose and let go of the mask. It should stay in place, held by the suction. (**2**) Put the mask on and adjust the headstrap, inhale through the nose and, if the mask seals, it should provide a good seal in the water. Get one with a shatterproof safety glass faceplate; the plastic ones fog up quickly and are easily scratched.

Security
Part of the team should land ahead of the main body to check that the beach is clear. Surfacing and removing their masks outside the surf zone, the security team goes ashore and signals 'Clear' to the rest of the troops when it has examined the beach area.

Disposal of the landing craft. This may mean destroying it, hiding it, or naval personnel ferrying it back to the mother ship.

Sanitization of the landing site and movement to the operational area.

The only common variation on this theme involves the use of indigenous craft – fishing boats, for example – which rendezvous with the mother ship some considerable distance off shore. Men and material can then be transferred, and infiltrated under cover of the boat's normal day-to-day activities.

Small boat handling is a specialised technique, and though it is part of general Special Forces training the unit commander will use the sea voyage to the disembarkation point to

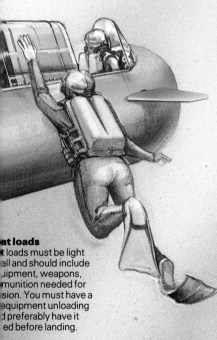

Swimmer delivery vehicle
The furthest reasonable distance the swimming team should have to cover is 1,500 metres. If the submarine cannot approach this close to the target area, then swimmer delivery vehicles should be used to reduce fatigue.

go over boat drill: transferring men and materials into the landing craft while underway, personnel recovery, communications drill and the use of special equipment such as the submarine escape trunk.

Physical exercise plays a big part in the shipboard life too, to ensure that the team is in top condition for the operation. This is a particular problem when the mother ship is a submarine making a completely submerged passage. The modern generation of submarines routinely cross oceans without ever surfacing, and there's not a lot of spare space on board for calisthenics and aerobic exercises!

Transferring at sea

From a surface ship, the transfer procedure is quite simple. The landing craft are inflated and sent over the side. A scrambling net is let down, and the operational team instal themselves in the inflatables, stow their equipment, and set off on their long journey to the beach.

Kit loads
Kit loads must be light ... all and should include ...uipment, weapons, ...munition needed for ...sion. You must have a ... equipment unloading ... preferably have it ...ed before landing.

Fins
A safety line can be attached to each swim fin and secured to your ankles to prevent you losing the fins if a strap breaks or if they are pulled from your feet by water action. Avoid fins with small or soft blades.

Knives
All swimmers should carry a knife with a corrosion-resistant blade such as stainless steel, and a rubber or plastic handle. Wooden handles have to be painted, oiled or waxed to waterproof them, which makes them fairly pointless, and cork or bone handles deteriorate rapidly when immersed in salt water.

And it will be a long journey. To maintain security, the mother ship will never come above the horizon, as seen from the shore – maybe a distance of more than 20 miles.

Outboard engines are notoriously noisy. There are electric versions which are almost silent, but they have a very limited range. To get around this problem the landing craft may be towed in close to shore by a purpose-built tug – low to the water and fitted with a heavily-silenced inboard engine. The landing craft then make their way the last two or three miles to

Some Special Forces equipment might seem to belong more on a James Bond movie set than with a real military unit, but mini-submarines and submersible dinghies are vital to undersea raiders like the SEALs.

UNDERWATER SEARCHING

An underwater search is normally conducted secretly, and is usually done to locate a lost object – e.g. a missile dropped by an aircraft that NATO does not want to fall into Soviet hands. The procedure for an underwater search is:

1 All kit must be totally prepared before entering the water.

2 All personnel must be fully briefed on the part they are to play in the search.

3 If water conditions are not ideal (good visibility, clear weather and current under 1 knot), rehearsals should be conducted if possible.

4 If the area has a muddy or loose sandy bottom, divers should take care to avoid stirring up the silt. They should remain more than 1 metre above the bottom if possible so that their fin movements do not disturb the bottom.

The creature from the Black Lagoon: a US Navy SEAL floats himself on to the beach armed with a 12-gauge pump-action shotgun for combat at point-blank range.

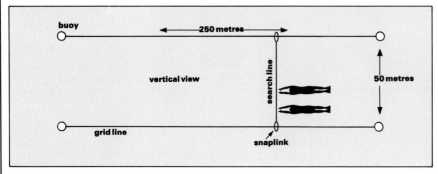

RUNNING JACK-STAY SEARCH

This is a fairly quick search technique used to find medium-sized or brightly coloured objects.

1 Only use in clear water

2 Use only experienced personnel

3 Requires one diver per 5 metres of line

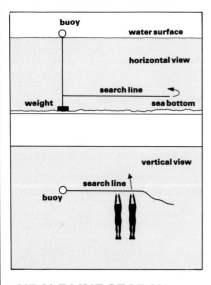

CIRCLE LINE SEARCH

This is another quick search technique, depending on the number of divers involved, and is useful in murky water or at night when searching for small objects. Inexperienced personnel can be used.

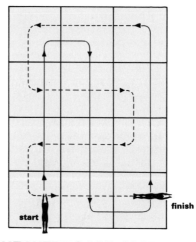

CHECKERBOARD JACK-STAY SEARCH

This is a variation of the jack-stay search used to locate small objects. In this method, the basic jack-stay system shown above is completed as normal, then the lines are taken up and placed perpendicular to the original lines and the search process repeated over the same area.

SHIPBOTTOM SEARCHES

When searching a friendly ship for mines:

1 Get a diagram of the hull from the ship's engineer.

2 Ensure that each diver knows the search procedure and objective before the dive.

3 Take a headcount of divers before starting.

4 Notify the ship's captain and harbour master before starting.

5 Wait for all machinery on the ship that might affect the dive to be shut down, especially vents, exhaust ports and engines.

6 Make sure that the sonar is turned off.

7 Once the vessel is ready, announce **"Divers underwater"**.

8 Start at the stern and work toward the bow, paying close attention to all hatches and vents. Be careful when in the vicinity of screws and salt water intakes.

9 If enemy mines are found, do not tamper with them but inform Navy Explosive Ordnance Disposal (EOD) personnel, who will deal with them.

10 Sweep the vessel several times if possible. Conduct a headcount of divers afterwards.

the beach under their own steam – or rather, by the muscle power of the Special Forces team who are paddling.

Transferring from a submarine to the landing craft is either a lot easier or a lot more difficult, depending on which one of the three methods is chosen. If the submarine can come to the surface, the inflatables can be dropped over the side, the landing party boards, and away they go. In one interesting variation to this method the boats are placed on the deck of the submarine and the crew get aboard then the submarine submerges gently beneath them.

Submarine landing

Alternatively, the submarine commander comes up to just below the surface, exposing only the very tip of the conning tower and presenting a very small picture, even to enemy radar. The landing party exits and either swims to the landing point, on a compass bearing, or inflates the boat in the water and paddles in.

The most secure technique of all requires the landing party to exit the submarine underwater, usually with the ship completely stationary and sitting on the bottom. Team members wearing SCUBA (Self-Contained Underwater Breathing Apparatus) then emerge from a hatch connected to an air-lock and swim under water to the landing place.

Special Forces personnel who undertake missions like this have to be highly trained and very, very fit. it's necessary to use this 'locking out echnique with technicians or mission specialists of any kind, who are not professional divers, then the lead pair will exit with inflatable boats and set them up on the surface. The rest of the team can then make 'free ascents' using the submarine's ordinary escape hatch, join up with the divers, and make their way to the beach in the normal way.

On the way in

In anything but a flat calm it will be impossible to see the shore for most of the journey in, except when you get up on to the crest of a wave. Even then, you probably won't have time to get a fix on your objective. You have to navigate by compass, and that's satisfactory as long as you know where you are.

Unfortunately, the seas and oceans never stand still. Except for a very short period at high and low tide (called 'slack water'), they are constantly in motion – and not just straight in to the beach and out again, either. On top of that there are coastal currents to contend with, and though they may run in the same direction all the time they certainly don't always run at the same speed.

These factors are much worse in some parts of the world than in others. The Mediterranean, for example, has no tides to speak of, while the Bay of Fundy and the Bristol Channel have up to 15 metres between low and high water. And around the Channel Islands they have four tides a day instead of two!

It's possible to compensate for all this, and the commander of the mother ship will have calculated the

transfer point to take account of all the known factors. Even so, the landing party will have to work hard to keep on course, and will be grateful for all the help they can get.

Find the beach

If there's no reception committee on the beach, the landing party will navigate for themselves, using the compass, sun or star sights and shoreline observation, and will be rather lucky to hit the beach at precisely the right place except in the easiest possible conditions.

If there is a beach party they can help with visible light, well shielded and only allowed to shine out to sea; infra-red beacons, which the boat party can pick up using special goggles; underwater sound, and radio.

The surf zone doesn't stretch very far out from the shore. When the landing party is close to its outer limit they

US Navy SEALs cling to their rubber dinghy as it is towed away from the coast at high speed by a cutter. You must minimise the time spent in transit between friendly vessel and enemy coast.

stop and maintain position. Scout swimmers get into the water, approach the beach and check it out. When they are sure there's no enemy activity they signal the rest of the party to come in.

There are no exceptions to this procedure. Even though there may be a reception committee waiting, with established perimeter security and reconnaissance patrols, the landing party still performs its own reconnaissance.

When searching for mines, lost missiles or equipment, you divide the area into manageable units using lengths of nylon rope. A systematic search can then begin, carefully examining each unit in turn. If time allows, search each one twice.

Combat Report

Vietnam:
Long Binh Patrol Part 2

Mike Glendon continues his story of engagement with the VC during a patrol in the Long Binh area, May 1969.

We woke up wet, tired and totally fed up. We had heard the VC in the night; it must have been a small patrol, but they didn't seem very concerned about their own security as they made no effort to keep their voices down and we could see them quite openly walking down the track next to us. But the skipper told us no contact was to be made, so off they went.

We moved a short distance away for chow and weapon cleaning. One of the forward scouts and the Sarge went to check out a junction that they had found on the move. At 07.30 we had just started to saddle up and move out when all hell broke loose. We dropped our packs and spread out.

On their way back from checking, Moose and the Sarge had turned a corner and literally bumped into two VC. Luckily they were relaxed and one of them had his AK-47 over his shoulder. Moose and the Sarge killed them instantly, but they received fire from their right flank. The enemy were in spider holes, which made them impossible to see, so we couldn't pinpoint their fire and it became difficult to cover our lads. We did it in the end: they got back OK fifteen minutes later, so the lead section was able to lay down some concentrated fire in the general direction of the VC.

Air strike

At 08.00 the skipper brought in a fire mission from the artillery on to the enemy. It was a bit worrying as he crept the barrage up to 30 metres in front of us and we had to put our packs on our heads. Then he put us into position for a second sweep; we were to go through the flank from which Moose and the Sarge had received fire. We were all feeling scared and vulnerable.

We started to move forward and at first we thought we were lucky, but then one rifle opened up. I moved forward. Jesus, I was so scared. Then I saw him, in an open foxhole about five metres in front, staring out to his front; and he looked bloody determined. What happened next seemed like a slow-motion film.

The VC must have sensed I was there. He

turned and saw me, bringing his AK-47 up. At the same time, without thinking, I got about ten rounds into him. He never made a sound, and the expression on his face never changed.

We were now receiving very heavy automatic fire from different foxholes and spider holes. The skipper called us back so that he could call in an air strike and so that we could wait for D Company to reinforce us.

One thing I'll say for the Yanks, they don't muck around with their firepower. At about 10.45 four Phantoms came in for the air strike, dropping high explosive and napalm, and Christ were they accurate.

Now we had to wait for D Company to be choppered in to reinforce us. It was so bloody quiet you could hear a fish fart. We counted the VC's KIAs. There were five: two were only youngsters. We couldn't afford to think about the morality of it all; we'd have gone insane.

At last, D Company arrived and moved up ahead of us. They were to go in first, as we were knackered. As soon as they got into position, Charlie opened up again, wounding three of them. We thought we must have run into a VC company that was well dug in. D Company had seen a few bunkers.

Getting the wounded

Our section plus a few other lads were sent in to get the three wounded guys. D Company were really getting the **** thrown at them. Our first job was to improve the clearing with C4 explosive so that the chopper could get in. If Charlie saw us we would be sitting ducks. As soon as we got into the clearing we started to receive fire, and some gook bastard seemed to have got a bead on me. I was lying behind an earth mound and every time I moved there was a hell of a crack beside my right ear. I couldn't work out where it was coming from.

One cheeky sod jumped into one of the foxholes that we'd already cleared. Deano pointed him out to me; there was only one way to get him. While Deano covered me I managed to get within throwing distance and blew the little bastard out with a grenade. Now we could get the wounded.

Christ, what a mess! One guy had his arm blown off at the elbow. He couldn't stay still, so we had to hold him down and run him, bent double, to our position at the clearing. He was swearing and cursing like a beast. We left him at the clearing: we had to move quickly to get the other WIA as the skipper had already called in the Dust-Off chopper.

But we were caught out. The VC pinned us down and we couldn't figure out where it was coming from. If only we had the GPMG. Then one of the other lads saw our situation, and he

and a few of his mates kept the VCs' heads down. This gave us the chance to get one of the wounded back to the makeshift chopper pad. He was in a bad way, with a sucking chest wound. When we got back, the other lads had brought in the body of another of the D Company guys. We wanted to get back into the fight ourselves, but we were needed to protect the chopper when it came in. There were no problems, and we moved up to D Company to cover their backs. They had done great.

We were stood to at 18.30, and later that night they brought in "Puff the Magic Dragon" a Dakota with six Miniguns that could put a bullet in every square inch of a football pitch. It left at 23.30. It was indescribable: thank God it was on our side.

The night wasn't too bad. Occasional sniping but that's all. When we woke up we were told that we were going to clear the VC bunkers out with another platoon of D Company. We were to move up at 10.00 hours. None of us had any appetite for breakfast. The waiting was terrible.

We moved up. No-one knew what our reception was going to be, and we were all pretty jumpy. There was a burst of automatic fire from one of the lead sections, but it came to nothing. We heard the culprit being bawled out from where we were. If the VC didn't know what we were up to before, they sure as hell did now.

We blow the bunker

We nearly fell over the first bunker we came to, and nearly wet our pants when we realised how close we had come. We were always amazed at how good Charlie was at concealing and camouflaging. After a very cautious check for booby traps we blew the bunker and found two bodies with weapons, which in this situation was unusual, as the VC usually drag their bodies away if given the time.

Just as I was approaching a blown spider hole next to another bunker, a gook ran off in front. He hadn't gone ten metres when Gary and I brought him down with a couple of bursts. The other platoon had found two gook WIAs who were given a rough time until their sergeant calmed everyone down; they also took one prisoner.

But the VC had done their normal trick of vanishing in the night, leaving behind a total of about 70 bodies with many blood trails, so there were obviously many more casualties carried off in the night. How the hell did they do it from right under our noses?

D Company went off to follow up the blood trails to see if they could find a VC camp. We returned to the fire support base, as we had to go out with the Yanks in a couple of days. We were absolutely knackered, and numbed with the ferocity and the suddenness with which the VC had hit us. We couldn't wait for the choppers to take us out. Two days off, even in an FSB, seemed absolute bliss. At 12.45 the choppers arrived, and so did the rain.

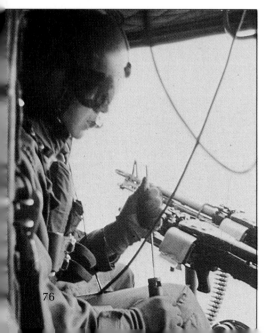

RIVER RAIDING

As he lowered himself into the filthy water of the canal, Hughes swore softly — it barely covered his chest. He settled the recirculating SCUBA gear and went down, not so much swimming as pulling himself along the bottom. That was dangerous, too – half a century's accumulation of rubbish down there, much of it sharp enough to cut your hand open in a flash. He set the waterproof stopwatch going and started off, trying to keep an even pace. Two miles to go to the power station...

He felt like he'd been down there for ever, but the watch said 50 minutes. Any time now he should feel the water temperature rising as the cooling water from the outlet flowed into the canal. Ah, there it was.

He closed the valves on the SCUBA and shrugged it off, anchoring it on the bottom with a collection of old iron and letting the tiny fishing float

areas possessing a dense network of inland waterways, small boats can provide a high degree of mobility for Special Forces combat teams.

bob to the surface. Then he made his way to the bank and slipped out silently...

Underwater operations

Infiltration is by no means the only type of amphibious operation. There are lots of important military targets underwater, in the water or close alongside, and all of these are vulnerable to attack from combat divers, either operating submerged or approaching secretly, landing, and approaching the target from an unexpected – and therefore poorly-guarded – direction.

Underwater operations like this generally require the diver to stay submerged for some considerable time, and that means breathing apparatus. There are two types of SCUBA: open circuit, where the bottles are filled with compressed air and the outbreath is vented into the water, and the closed circuit system, where the diver breathes the same air over and over again, each breath being 'topped up' with pure oxygen carried in the

CHOOSING A LANDING PLACE

The ideal site for a sea-borne landing has very similar features to a good airborne drop zone: it's easy to identify from a distance; is free of obstacles; has good and secure access and evacuation routes for both the transportation group and the reception committee; and is largely free from enemy activity. The main differences lie in the sea, and under it.

Any reasonably competent observer can evaluate an inland drop zone just by looking around carefully. To do the same for a sea-borne landing requires a certain amount of training in the science of hydrography. Tides and currents are more difficult to deal with than underwater obstacles – at least these don't move around all the time!

Navigation at sea or even on inland waterways is much more difficult than on land, chiefly because it's difficult to know exactly where you are at all times. Modern small radar equipment can solve this problem, but leaves you exposed if the enemy detects the radar emissions.

A better solution is offered by satellite navigation (satnav) hardware, which will tell you where you are to within 100 metres anywhere on the earth's surface. Because it's completely passive (it transmits nothing itself, but only receives), you don't risk giving away your position when you use it.

RIVER RECCE TECHNIQUES

Small boats enable you to carry far more weapons and equipment than you could move on foot, and in areas with a large inland waterway network you are often more mobile than units travelling by land

1 Crew of boat B observes and covers A

2 Crew of boat A observes, signals B forward if clear, and covers B as it passes to next point

3 When B reaches selected point it observes and signals A forward if clear

debarked troops

debarked troops

Movement by alternate bounds
This is the quicker recce method using two boats, but does not allow the second boat to observe carefully before passing the leading boat.

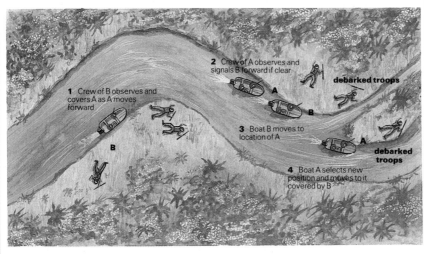

1 Crew of B observes and covers A as A moves forward

2 Crew of A observes and signals B forward if clear

3 Boat B moves to location of A

4 Boat A selects new position and moves to it covered by B

debarked troops

debarked troops

Movement by successive bounds
This is slower but more thorough: use this technique when you are expecting enemy contact.

tanks and the exhaled carbon dioxide absorbed by a special chemical.

Closed circuit SCUBA is particularly difficult and dangerous to use, and even preparing the equipment is risky in itself – pure oxygen is highly explosive in the right circumstances. The advantage is that it doesn't leave a stream of tell-tale bubbles to give away the diver's position.

Demolition charges

Even with the danger of being spotted, open circuit SCUBA can sometimes be used, but the surface of the water must be broken and turbulent to minimise the risk. The advantage is in its ease of use and much greater safety.

As well as laying demolition charges, the combat diver may be called upon to reconnoitre minefields and other underwater obstacles, check out harbours, docks and dams, establish and recover underwater caches of equipment, and find essential equipment that has had to be abandoned in an emergency.

Because it's bulky and difficult to conceal, equipment for underwater missions will have to be air-dropped to established undercover Special Forces teams as they need it.

Small boat operations

In many countries rivers and inland waterways take the place of roads as the prime communication routes, and Special Forces, with their comprehensive training, are very well equipped to make good use of them.

River craft and small inflatables are

etter suited to transportation than for use as fighting vehicles, though you must always be prepared for ambushes, for example, which will force you to fight from the boat. This possibility will influence the team leader's decision when it comes to choosing between boats or travelling overland.

The one great advantage to travelling by boat is the speed. It's quite in order to estimate average speeds of 25 to 30 miles an hour in areas where the waterways are widely used and kept free of debris and other obstructions.

Inflatable boats

Inflatables, which ride on top of the water, are much more manoeuvrable than displacement craft, which may draw anything up to two-thirds of a metre. They are also very light in

US Navy SEALS and accompanying South Vietnamese troops prepare to go ashore in the Mekong Delta. When fighting against guerrillas, **Special Forces** units often use local boats.

weight, and so can be carried for short distances if necessary.

Purpose-built inflatable assault boats do have their disadvantages, however. There's no disguising them; their outboard engines make an awful

THE RAID GOES ASHORE

The transit to the area may take some time, and distance will depend entirely on fuel consumption. The troops must also be prepared for a wet and bumpy ride and must wear adequate clothing.

At a certain distance from the objective the boats slow their engines to cut down on noise. At this point their greatest ally will be wind and the crash of the sea, which will disguise any noise they make. From there they move slowly up to a rendezvous point within a visible distance of their landing site. It is important to note that good radar can pick up and identify small boats, and you should remember this when planning the route.

Once at this RV point the troops wait for a pre-arranged signal from the reconnaissance team ashore to notify them that all is clear to move in. It may be that something has occurred ashore and therefore no signal will be given, in which case the boats will return.

Having received the signal, the boats move in with engines cut and the troops paddling. This depends on weather conditions, but it is essential that from here on as little sound as possible is made. One man in each boat has a gun trained on the shore as a precaution. Once in, everyone disembarks as quickly and quietly as possible and moves to a given area to await the next stage. Meanwhile, the boats wait in the most concealed area, along with a guard force, their bows pointing back out to sea.

The raiding force commander and his team

If the target is actually on the river, an assault team can receive fire support from the water: here a **US Navy PBR** prepares to land a **SEAL** team. In the bows is a 7.62-mm Minigun capable of firing 6,000 rounds per minute.

leaders are then given a final brief by the recce team commander. This gives everyone an opportunity to confirm any last-minute details and to make any changes. Once everyone is satisfied, the team leaders move off to brief their teams and then, at a given time, they move off.

It may be necessary at this stage for teams to split and approach the target from different angles. In this case, each team is led by one member of the recce force, who takes them up to a starting line. Quite often the recce team acts as a fire support group, giving whatever help they can when required.

lot of noise, and they are very easily damaged by waterlogged trees and other debris floating on or close to the surface.

When he decides whether or not to use boats in a particular operation, the team leader has to think of the operation as a whole, and choose the ways and means most likely to get the job done successfully and in the shortest possible time.

The rule of thumb must be: use boats when they offer a quicker way of getting from place to place; abandon them and set off across country when that looks like the better solution. The same applies to using divers: hit the enemy where he's weakest, from the direction he'll least expect.

This training in small boats and underwater operations is just one more example of the flexibility of the Special Forces soldier, ready to go anywhere and do anything at a moment's notice.

RAIDING A SHORE INSTALLATION

The first priority when mounting a raid on the enemy coast is to carry out a thorough recce of the target area; it is unusual for you to have enough information available without sending in a reconnaissance team. They will be looking for the following:

1 The exact location, size and structure of the target.

2 Any fortifications, minefields, searchlights and wandering guard patrols, checking their routines.
3 The nature of the surrounding terrain.
4 The best route from the sea to the target.
5 A place where the boats can come in and be hidden while the attack goes in.
6 A position to place any covering fire or mortar teams.

Cratering charges

This mixture of five charges at 1.5 m and 2.1 m depth will blow a crater approximately 2.5 metres deep and 7.5 metres wide in any road.

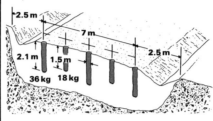

Timber cutting charges

If you can drill into the wood and place the explosives inside, you can use a much smaller charge.

For exterior explosives, calculate the charge using the formula D^2 divided by 40. (D = least dimension in inches). This gives the number of pounds of TNT needed.

SCUBA attack
If the enemy has prepared his position for defence against waterborne attack, try a diversionary overland attack by debarked troops while a small team goes in underwater using SCUBA gear.

Covering fire
If it is available, use mortar or artillery fire to cover the retreat of the raiding force after the attack. You can also set an ambush along the river bank to attack any enemy who pursue you along the waterways.

Powerplant
Motor-powered boats can accelerate quickly to over 30 mph, but they are extremely noisy and should be used only if secrecy is no longer a consideration. Also remember that outboard motors need constant care and maintenance, so have a good supply of spare parts available. Due to their high fuel consumption you will need to plan your fuel supply carefully.

AMBUSHING BOATS

In many ways, it's easier to ambush a boat than it is a foot patrol or even a team of armoured personnel carriers. Boats can't leave the track and disappear into the bush. Very few boats carry armour capable of stopping even a GPMG round.

But there is one additional factor that you have to consider: unlike a road or a track, the river may change its characteristics considerably between the time you plan the ambush and the time you carry the operation out. This is particularly noticeable and important in tidal waters, of course.

These changes in the depth of water available, and even in the direction in which it flows, can affect you in two ways: it may cause the enemy to travel by a different route, making your stake-out a complete waste of time. But it may also cut off your retreat, and leave you exposed to retaliation by a much stronger force.

Treat your own boats as transport craft, not fighting platforms, and disembark the troops who are going to form the ambush party. Boat crews will stay with the craft, which should be kept ready for start-up.

When you choose a site for an ambush on land, one of the most important factors is the killing ground – the place to which the enemy is going to run when you open fire on him. The same sort of consideration doesn't apply in a river ambush. The only way he can leave the boats is by going over the side, and a well-aimed fragmentation grenade barrage will make that a very costly business.

The only other escape route he's got is to get his boats out, and the stop groups placed at each end of the ambush site should take care of that.

The only sure way to deal with a river ambush is to see it before you get into it, and that means constant patrol activity out ahead of the main force – along the banks as well as on the water.

In areas where the enemy is known to be operating, the wise commander uses his boats and his men in very much the same way as an APC platoon commander uses his vehicles, using bounding overwatch to make his progress as safe and secure as possible.

Approach on foot
If the objective is some distance from the shore, a boat-borne team may debark and approach stealthily on foot. This permits a more thorough search of the area and, in the event of contact, friendly fire and manoeuvre will be faster and more effective.

RIVER RAIDERS

When your objective is near the banks of a river you can use motor-driven boats to storm directly into the objective area. However, this is a bold and potentially dangerous tactic and should only be used when you can take the enemy by surprise and the waterway is large enough for your boats to perform evasive action if they come under fire. Here, an assault force retreats downriver after taking out a shore installation.

Enemy reaction
Try to avoid a situation where your assault team comes under fire while in its boats. You are a closely-packed and easy target even if you do have room to manoeuvre the boat; this is why blocking forces should be dropped off to cover your withdrawal.

Automatic weapons
If you do come under fire while in the boat you must withdraw rapidly unless you are able to debark very quickly. Try to suppress the enemy with as much automatic fire as you can muster while the boat retreats out of range. Here the SEAL is using a Stoner LMG, an experimental weapons system popular with some Special Forces units in Vietnam.

Boat capabilities
For amphibious raids boats can
(**1**) move troops to the objective;
(**2**) position blocking forces to stop enemy forces reacting to the attack;
(**3**) provide suppressive fire for the assault team;
(**4**) protect the flanks of the assault team while it goes in

BLOWING UP BRIDGES

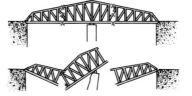

1 For complicated structures, two sets of cutting charges are required to cause collapse of the bridge. These should not be placed equidistant from the central support.

3 Stone arch bridges are best demolished by placing a charge to blow out the keystones. A larger gap will be created using three charges placed as shown.

2 Cutting charges must be placed on beams and crossbraces as well as on the floor plating.

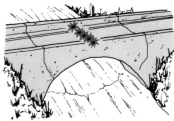

4 Small stone arch spans are easily demolished by a row of cutting charges across the centre, which destroys the integrity of the arch.

The diagrams above show where to place a line of charges on some typical bridges. Remember that only one person should prepare, place and fire explosive charges – never divide responsibility; this is how expensive mistakes can occur. To destroy a bridge abutment use 18-kg TNT charges in holes 1.5 metres deep at 1.5-metre intervals across the width of the bridge, and 1.5 metres behind the river face of the abutment.

Unarmed Combat Course No.5

DEFENCE AGAINST WRISTHOLDS

Pull-up with two-handed support

An amateur attacker will almost always move in close — and then he'll grab you. Most often, he'll get hold of you by the wrists, thinking he can stop you throwing a punch and then overpower you. He'll be wrong. This section of the Unarmed Combat Course shows you some quick, simple and effective counter-moves to such an assault. These techniques can be used against wristholds from the front, and are an important part of your total defence strategy.

This is used when the attacker grabs you with both his thumbs on top.

1 The attacker seizes one of your wrists.

2 Quickly reach over with your free hand and grasp your other hand.

3 Pull sharply upwards against the attacker's thumbs.

4 You can follow this with an elbow strike to his jaw.

Pull-up against attacker's thumb

This is used against an attacker who grips you by the wrist.

Pull the wrist he's holding towards your body with a vigorous action.

Push your wrist sharply against your attacker's thumb.

Pass hands & knuckle smash

Sometimes the attacker will grasp both your wrists

Force your hands inwards so that they cross each other.

As the assailant tries to force them apart, smash his knuckles together.

Smashing the attacker's hand against a wall

This is useful when an attack takes place in a built-up area next to a house or wall. When the attacker grasps your wrist, drive the back of his knuckles against a wall to make him release his grip.

Flip-over and pull down with newspaper

This is very effective if you're carrying a rolled-up newspaper or umbrella.

1 When the attacker seizes your wrist, immediately turn your hand inwards, bending his arm.

2 Grab the end of the newspaper in your other hand.

3 Force the attacker downwards onto the ground. This must all be done very quickly before the attacker has a chance to react and let go.

83

DEFENCE AGAINST HOLDS FROM THE REAR

If you are grabbed from behind without warning you must react immediately and instinctively. The following techniques should be used to fight your way free the one you use depends largely on whether the attacker has grabbed you under or over your arms.

Grasp little finger and bend

1 At least one of the attacker's little fingers will be free. Grab it as hard as you can.

2 By bending back the little finger you should be able to force the attacker to let you go.

3 If he hangs on, twist down and round, which will break his finger unless he releases you.

Double elbow strike

1 Stretch and reach upwards to allow yourself some free movement.

2 Hold one of your wrists with your other hand and bend away from the attacker.

3 Swing yourself violently around and deliver an elbow strike to the attacker's head. If his grip is not broken immediately carry on round and strike again from the other side.

Grasp or blow to the scrotum

If the attacker's arms are over yours, twist and reach down.

2 Then try to strike or, preferably, grasp the attacker's testicles.

Reach for the pressure points

Drop your body weight, reach up, and press your middle fingers hard against the pressure points located below your attacker's ears. Follow up with a shin scrape.

3 Grab his testicles, twist and squeeze hard. This should make him lose interest in attacking you, but if he hangs on, continue to lean forward.

4 Bring your head back smartly to deliver a head-butt to his face.

5 Follow up with a shin scrape, and a stamp on his foot.

Unarmed Combat Course No. 7
DEFENCE AGAINST HOLDS FROM THE REAR PART 2

Drop, take ankle and throw backwards

These are two advanced defences against a rear hold. An instant and aggressive reaction on your part can turn the tables on the attacker and allow you to take the initiative.

1 The attacker grabs you from behind. Immediately you begin to move your feet apart.

2 Bend your legs and reach between them to grab the attacker's ankle.

3 Drive yourself upwards using your leg muscles, and pull his foot forward at the same time.

4 Complete the counter-attack by stamping on his testicles.

Arms over, drop and throw forwards

Again, the attacker grabs you from behind. You must act without hesitation.

2 Bring up your arms and clamp them over the attacker's arms.

3 Bend your knees to get under the attacker's centre of gravity.

4 Pull hard on his arms while bending forwards.

5 Kneel down on the throwing side and the attacker will be thrown over your shoulder.

Scoring with the SCORPION

The Scorpion is one of the fastest tracked vehicles in the world. Armed with a 76-mm gun and powered by a Jaguar 4.2-litre engine, it can outrun anything it cannot outfight. Although its true purpose is to scout ahead of British units it is not restricted to this reconnaissance role; in the Falklands, in Thailand and in Iran Scorpions have fought as light tanks, using their weapons in direct support of the infantry.

In the British Army the Scorpion is officially designated CVT(T) or Combat Vehicle Reconnaissance (Tracked). Its role is quite different to that of Main Battle Tanks such as the Chieftain and Challenger; relying on its speed and manoeuvrability, the Scorpion acts as the eyes and ears of British commanders. Its primary mission is to gather an up-to-date picture of enemy strengths and intentions. If it is detected by the enemy it will usually withdraw rather than stand and fight – there is no future in tangling with enemy tanks.

Crew skills

The Scorpion is very lightly armoured, and its real defence against enemy fire is the skill of the three-man crew. Taking advantage of every hill or fold in the ground, they must see but not be seen.

The crew consists of a driver, a gunner and a commander who also doubles as a loader. The driver enters his tiny compartment via a large single-piece hatch cover, in front of which is a single wide-angle periscope for driving in the closed-down position.

Night driving

Although the powerplant wall to the right of the driver is covered by special padding to help absorb noise, you can hear very little above the high-pitched roar of the engine.

The Scorpion, like most tracked vehicles, is steered not by a steering wheel but by two tillers, or sticks, positioned in front of the driver. To go left, the left tiller is pulled back; to go right, the right tiller is pulled back. This makes one track go faster than the other, and so makes the vehicle turn, and is very easy after little instruction. There are three foot pedals from left to right, a gear selector, brake and accelerator, plus a ratchet handbrake.

On entering the vehicle the driver adjusts his seat to the correct position before carrying out his pre-start up checks. Unlike most civilian vehicles,

Scimitars of the Blues and Royals played an important role in the Falklands campaign despite their small numbers. They covered an average of 350 miles each, and performed very well over the boggy ground.

Each British tank regiment has eight Scorpions, whose job is to scout ahead of the Main Battle Tanks. The RAF Regiment also uses Scorpions for airfield defence.

Above: The Scorpion family is designed to operate in temperatures from −30°C to +50°C. These Scimitars are on exercise in Norway with NATO's ACE mobile force.

Below: A Scorpion stands ready to pull a member of the Alvis 600 series of 6×6 vehicles upright. In the Falklands the Scorpions and Scimitars frequently pulled each other out of boggy terrain.

This is the most heavily-armed member of the Scorpion family, carrying a 90-mm Cockerill gun. Malaysia has bought about 26 of this version.

there is a safety device incorporated into the transmission that makes certain the engine will not start if the vehicle is in gear.

The driver always wears a helmet, firstly for safety reasons — there are many sharp corners in the vehicle where you can knock yourself — and secondly because it contains the intercom that is the vital link between the commander and the driver.

Then the driver switches the power on and tests the radio, and the commander gives the order to move out. The driver selects first or second gear, releases the handbrake and, with a gentle press on the accelerator, the vehicle moves smoothly off.

The ability to move quickly from one position to another is vital for a reconnaissance vehicle, and Scorpion moves so rapidly that the commander

and driver have to brace themselves to avoid injury, especially when moving at speed over rough terrain.

The Scorpion's gear unit is a semi-automatic transmission with seven speeds in each direction, and all the driver has to do to change gear is to push his heel down to change up through the gears and his toe to change down. This gives you slightly more control than you would get with fully automatic – for example, when about to go up a slope you can change down before starting to travel uphill.

Use of ground

Although the driver takes his orders from the commander in the turret, he decides how to use the ground to avoid being detected, for example keeping off the tops of hills and avoiding deep mud, which could bog the vehicle down. As was demonstrated in the Falklands campaign, the Scorpion has a very low ground pressure compared to many other armoured vehicles, and this allows it to operate in terrain that would otherwise be impassable.

The driver is constantly reading the ground ahead to provide the smoothest possible ride. As he is low down he doesn't feel the bumps that make the other two crew members hang on for grim death.

The Scorpion's main armament is a 76-mm gun. It fires HESH (High Explosive Squash Head), HE (High Explosive), smoke and illuminating rounds, plus training rounds. With

Inside the Scorpion

The Scorpion is one of the most agile combat vehicles in service today; its light weight and powerful engine allow it to accelerate from 0-30 mph (48 km/h) in 16 seconds. Its ground pressure is less than that of a walking man, which allows it to operate over relatively boggy ground.

Gunner
the gunner has two periscopes, a roof-mounted sight and a passive night sight which can detect enemy infra-red device. The gun controls include hand elevation and a manual, two-speed traverse.

Suspension
The torsion bar suspension consists of five aluminium road wheels with rubber tyres; the first and last wheels have hydraulic shock absorbers. The tracks are light steel and have an average life of 3,000 miles.

The Scorpion Family

Striker is the anti-tank member of the Scorpion family, carrying five Swingfire missiles with a range of 4,000 metres.

Spartan is an armoured personnel carrier based on the same chassis, and carries four infantrymen in the back.

Samson is the armoured recovery model and can pull 12 tonnes with its heavy-duty winch.

Samaritan is an armoured ambulance, and the same hull is used for the armoured command vehicle, Sultan.

the advent of new types of tank armour, the HESH round has lost much of its effectiveness against heavier armoured vehicles, but it is still effective against the sides of tanks, lighter armoured vehicles and field fortifications. A total of 40 rounds of 76-mm ammunition are carried. A 7.62-mm machine gun is mounted co-axial with the main armament and this can also be used as a ranging machine-gun. A total of 3000 rounds are carried for it.

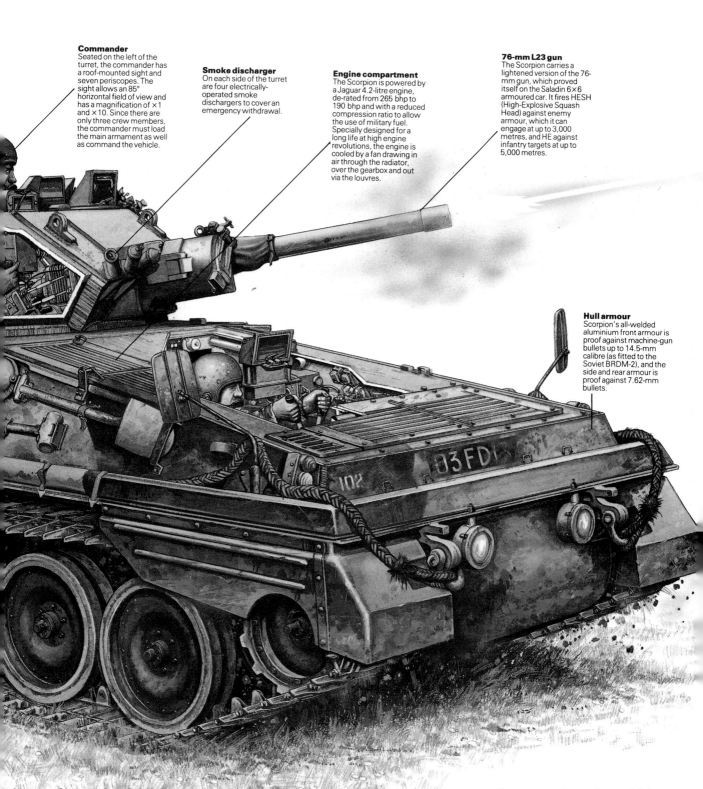

Commander
Seated on the left of the turret, the commander has a roof-mounted sight and seven periscopes. The sight allows an 85° horizontal field of view and has a magnification of ×1 and ×10. Since there are only three crew members, the commander must load the main armament as well as command the vehicle.

Smoke discharger
On each side of the turret are four electrically-operated smoke dischargers to cover an emergency withdrawal.

Engine compartment
The Scorpion is powered by a Jaguar 4.2-litre engine, de-rated from 265 bhp to 190 bhp and with a reduced compression ratio to allow the use of military fuel. Specially designed for a long life at high engine revolutions, the engine is cooled by a fan drawing in air through the radiator, over the gearbox and out via the louvres.

76-mm L23 gun
The Scorpion carries a lightened version of the 76-mm gun, which proved itself on the Saladin 6×6 armoured car. It fires HESH (High-Explosive Squash Head) against enemy armour, which it can engage at up to 3,000 metres, and HE against infantry targets at up to 5,000 metres.

Hull armour
Scorpion's all-welded aluminium front armour is proof against machine-gun bullets up to 14.5-mm calibre (as fitted to the Soviet BRDM-2), and the side and rear armour is proof against 7.62-mm bullets.

Mounted on each side of the turret is a bank of four electrically-operated smoke dischargers; when fired these enable the vehicle to quickly withdraw under the cover of smoke.

Scimitar is armed with a .30 mm RARDEN cannon. This fires Armour Piercing Discarding Sabot (APDS), Armour Piercing Secondary Effect (APSE) and High Explosive Incendiary (HEI), all of which have a tracer element to enable the gunner to follow the fall of shot. The APDS is the latest round and has been designed to penetrate light enemy vehicles such as the BMP-2, although it would also go through the hull sides and rear of Main Battle Tanks.

Versatile family

In addition to the Scorpion and Scimitar, a whole family of vehicles has been designed using the same basic automotive components: obviously an advantage to the Army. Other vehicles in the family include the Spartan armoured personnel carrier, which has also been adopted for many specialised roles (for example anti-tank with two Milan missiles in the ready-to-launch position, and anti-aircraft with four Javelin surface-to-air missiles in ready to launch position); Samaritan armoured ambulance; Sultan armoured command vehicle; Samson armoured recovery vehicle; Striker anti-tank vehicle; and Streaker high mobility load carrier. Further development has resulted in the Stormer

armoured personnel carrier, whic[h] forms the basic member of a complet[e] family of some 20 vehicles.

Scorpion is also available with [a] more fuel efficient diesel engine i[n] place of the petrol engine and a full[y] automatic transmission, plus a host o[f] other options including powered tu[r]ret controls, different fire control sys[s]tems, laser rangefinder and so o[n]. More recently a 90-mm gun has bee[n] fitted in place of the 76-mm weapo[n] and this model has already bee[n]

Above: The Scorpion is one of the lightes[t] tracked combat vehicles in the world. It is air-portable, and is seen here being lifted by a Chinook helicopter. Two can be fitte[d] inside a Hercules aircraft.

Battlefield Evaluation: comparing

Scorpion

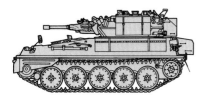

The Scorpion family of armoured vehicles has proved very successful: in addition to the British Army versions, Malaysia has bought 26 fitted with 90-mm guns, and many other armies now operate Scorpions modified to suit local requirements. In the Falklands the Scorpions and Scimitars managed very well over the boggy ground, and one withstood a shell exploding just 1½ metres away.

Specification:
Combat weight: 8 tonnes
Maximum road speed: 80 km/h
Power to weight ratio: 23.5 hp/tonne
Length: 4.7 m
Height: 2.1 m
Crew: 3
Armament: 1x76-mm gun; 1x7.62-mm machine-gun

Assessment
Firepower   ★★★★
Protection   ★★★
Age   ★★★
Worldwide users   ★★★★

Light and compact, the Scorpion's outstanding cross-country mobility makes it excellent for reconnaissance.

ENGESA EE-9 Cascavel

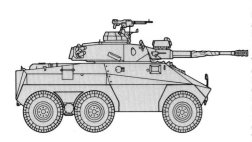

Produced by Brazil the EE-9 has been widely exported and is seeing action in the interminable Gulf War with Iraqi armoured reconnaissance units. Wheeled vehicles are much cheaper than track layers like the Scorpion and their cross-country performance is not that inferior. Its 90-mm gun gives the EE-9 a respectable anti-tank capability and the latest vehicles supplied to Iraq have laser rangefinders.

Specification:
Combat weight: 13.7 tonnes
Maximum road speed: 100 km/h
Power to weight ratio: 15.5 hp/tonne
Length: 5.2 m
Height: 2.6 m
Crew: 3
Armament: 1x90-mm gun, 1x7.62-mm and 1x.50 cal Browning machine-gun

Assessment
Firepower   ★★★★
Protection   ★★
Age   ★★
Worldwide users   ★★★

The Brazilian Cascavel combines goo[d] anti-tank capacity with rugged simplicity and attractive price.

AMX-13

The AMX-13 light tank was developed by the French immediately after World War II and is still in production. Originally armed with a 75-mm gun, most vehicles were re-equipped with a 90-mm weapon and the model currently offered for export carries a 105-mm gun. The Israelis used some AMX-13s in the 1967 Six-Day War, but they had a disagreeable experience when they tried to take on Soviet-supplied T-54/55 Main Battle Tanks.

Specification:
Combat weight: 17 tonnes
Maximum road speed: 60 km/h
Power to weight ratio: 16.6 hp/tonne
Length: 4.9 m
Height: 2.3 m
Crew: 3
Armament: 1x105-mm gun; 1x7.62-mm machine-gun

Assessment
Firepower   ★★★★★
Protection   ★★★
Age   ★★★★★
Worldwide users   ★★★★

The ageing AMX-13 is still in production, now mounting a semi-automatic 105-mm gun.

dopted by a number of countries.

Since production started at Alvis in Coventry in 1972 over 3500 members of the Scorpion family have been built for sale to almost 20 armies in virtually every corner of the world. It is even used by the British Royal Air Force Regiment to defend its four key airfields in West Germany against attack from Soviet paratroops and special forces.

A Scimitar of the Blues and Royals dug in in the Falklands where several vehicles used their 30-mm RARDEN cannon against Argentine aircraft, one claiming a hit on a Skyhawk at a range of 1,000 metres.

the Scorpion with its rivals

AMX-10RC

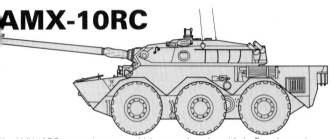

The AMX-10RC reconnaissance vehicle entered service with the French army in 1979. Armed with a semi-automatic 105-mm gun, it is perfectly capable of knocking out Main Battle Tanks but its cost has proved a major problem and the French army had reduced its order from 525 to 284 vehicles. The AMX-10RC is fully amphibious, being propelled in the water by two water-jets, and it has an NBC defensive system.

Specification:
Combat weight: 15.8 tonnes
Maximum road speed: 85 km/h
Power to weight ratio: 16.45 hp/tonne
Length: 6.3 m
Height: 2.7 m
Crew: 4
Armament: 1x105-mm gun; 1x7.62-mm machine-gun

Assessment
Firepower   ★★★★★
Protection   ★★
Age   ★★
Worldwide users   ★★

The AMX-10RC has been tested in the Chadian civil war, and is being adopted by the French army.

BRDM-2

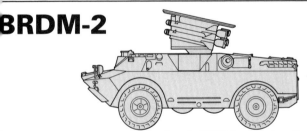

Soviet reconnaissance battalions rely heavily on the BRDM-2 armoured car. One version carries a turret with a 14.5-mm heavy machine-gun and a co-axial 7.62-mm weapon; the other main variant has launcher rails for six AT-3 'Sagger' anti-tank missiles instead. In addition to the two-man crew, the BRDM-2s in the reconnaissance units often carry two infantrymen with a machine-gun and an RPG-7 anti-tank rocket.

Specification:
Combat weight: 7 tonnes
Maximum road speed: 100 km/h
Power to weight ratio: 20 hp/tonne
Length: 5.75 m
Height: 2.3 m with turret; 2.0 m without
Crew: 2-4
Armament: 1x14.5-mm and 1x7.62-mm machine-guns or 6 'Sagger' ATGMs
Assessment
Firepower   ★★★
Protection   ★
Age   ★★★
Worldwide users   ★★★★

The standard BRDM-2 has a 14.5-mm HMG, but the Scorpion's frontal armour is proof against this.

Spähpanzer Luchs

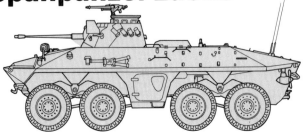

The Luchs entered service with the West German army in 1975 and soon established a reputation for excellent cross-country mobility. The commander and gunner occupy the turret and a fourth crew member sits to the rear of the turret, operating the radio. In an emergency he can take control of the vehicle.

Specification:
Combat weight: 19.5 tonnes
Maximum road speed: 90 km/h
Power to weight ratio: 20 hp/tonne
Length: 7.74 m
Height: 2.1 m
Crew: 4
Armament: 1x20-mm cannon; 1x7.62-mm machine-gun

Assessment
Firepower   ★★
Protection   ★★
Age   ★★
Worldwide users   ★

The Luchs is enormous, following the German World War II tradition of large 8×8 armoured cars.

ENTER THE DRAGON

Anti-tank guided missiles — weapons for killing tanks on the battlefield — were one of the many bright ideas that came out of Germany in World War II. The first one, known as X-7 and later as 'Rotkäppchen' (Little Red Riding Hood), was developed in 1944-5. Work had not finished when the war ended, and the idea was taken up in France, Britain and the USA, all of whom produced missiles in the mid-1950s. These were all 'first generation' wire-guided missiles; the operator fired them off, then steered them by means of a joystick or similar

Once Dragon's sights tell you when an enemy tank is within range, release the safety catch and press the trigger. Now you must keep the target in your sights. The micro-computer will control the missile's course to make sure it hits the target.

SELECTING A FIRING POSITION

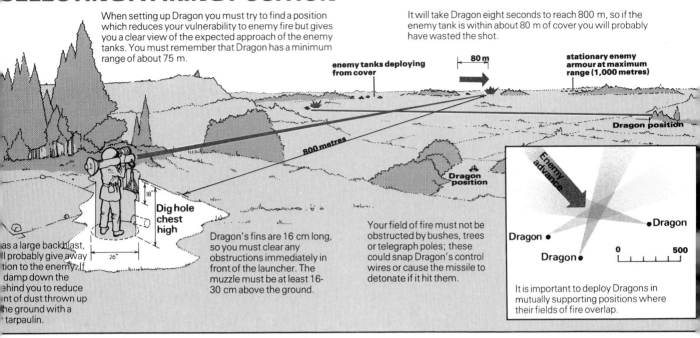

When setting up Dragon you must try to find a position which reduces your vulnerability to enemy fire but gives you a clear view of the expected approach of the enemy tanks. You must remember that Dragon has a minimum range of about 75 m.

It will take Dragon eight seconds to reach 800 m, so if the enemy tank is within about 80 m of cover you will probably have wasted the shot.

enemy tanks deploying from cover

80 m

stationary enemy armour at maximum range (1,000 metres)

Dragon position

800 metres

Dragon position

Dig hole chest high

18

26"

as a large backblast, l probably give away tion to the enemy. If damp down the ehind you to reduce nt of dust thrown up he ground with a tarpaulin.

Dragon's fins are 16 cm long, so you must clear any obstructions immediately in front of the launcher. The muzzle must be at least 16-30 cm above the ground.

Your field of fire must not be obstructed by bushes, trees or telegraph poles; these could snap Dragon's control wires or cause the missile to detonate if it hit them.

Enemy advance

Dragon •

Dragon •

• Dragon

Dragon •

0   500

It is important to deploy Dragons in mutually supporting positions where their fields of fire overlap.

---

control, his commands being signalled down the wire to the missile.

The first-generation missiles demanded highly-skilled and well-practised operators. In order to reduce the need for skill, the manufacturers set about developing the 'second generation'. These rely upon the sight unit actually tracking the missile in some way or other, and generating automatic corrections. All the firer has to do is keep his sight on the target and the automatic circuits do the rest, steering the missile until it hits.

Laser beam

The drawback to all these systems is the need to drag wire behind the missile in order to send the correction signals, and one or two modern missiles have done away with this, using a laser beam instead. The missile senses the beam and keeps steering itself in line with it, so that as long as the operator keeps the beam on the target, the missile will eventually hit it.

The snag is that, once fired, the operator must keep tracking his target until the missile hits, which may be as long as 15 or 25 seconds – time in which he can be spotted and shot at. And, as the Israelis proved in the 1973 war, if you can upset a missile operator by zipping a few rounds of machine-gun fire past his ear, he is highly likely to lose concentration and thus miss the target.

Development of Dragon was begun

Dragon operators must remain stationary and concentrate for up to 11 seconds, so they need other infantrymen to provide close security in order to operate successfully.

In carrying mode, Dragon weighs just under 15 kg. Its deployment depends on the tactical situation, but ideally several weapons should be placed in mutually supporting positions.

Dragon lives up to its name and breathes fire as the missile blasts off on its way. However, the main giveaway is the huge backblast, which tells everyone where you are.

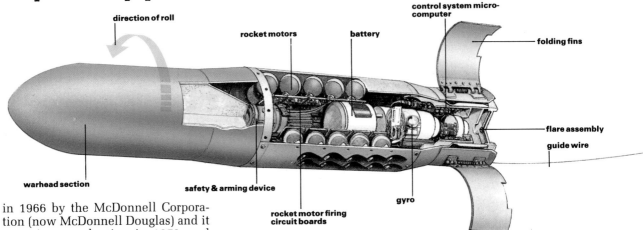

direction of roll

rocket motors

battery

control system micro-computer

folding fins

flare assembly

guide wire

gyro

rocket motor firing circuit boards

safety & arming device

warhead section

in 1966 by the McDonnell Corporation (now McDonnell Douglas) and it went into production in 1972, and into service with the US Army in Europe in 1976. It is a tube-launched, wire-guided, optically-tracked missile operated by one man. The front end of the launcher tube is supported on a light stand, the rest of the weight being taken by the firer on his shoulder.

The missile is pre-packed inside the launcher, and on the outside of the tube is the 'tracker', a combined sight unit and electronics package.

Strange steering

The unusual part about Dragon is the method of propulsion and steering. The missile is in three sections; at the front is the shaped charge warhead, which is said to be capable of defeating 400 mm of armour or 1 metre of reinforced concrete. The mid-section carries 60 side-thrust rocket motors and the rear section carries the wire dispenser, the electronics, the battery and an infra-red flare, and three folding fins.

When the firer spots a target he

Dragon's warhead could take out any Soviet tank in existence when it first appeared, but the latest generation of Soviet armour is much better protected against chemical energy weapons.

Inside the Dragon

Dragon is very accurate against stationary targets at up to 1000 metres, but against moving vehicles it is most effective between 200 and 800 metres. It takes several seconds to get the missile under control s if the target is too close you may well miss. US infantry use LAW 66-mm anti-tank rockets against enem armour within Dragon's minimum range. You cannot conceal the huge backblast of the weapon but you can try to confuse the enemy by setting up dummy positions and using smoke grenades or grenade simulators.

dumps the stand on the ground, squats behind it with the tube on his shoulder, and takes aim. The missile's maximum range is 1,000 metres, and a marker in the sight helps range estimation. As soon as the target appears to be within range, the firer presses a thumb-switch safety catch and squeezes the trigger.

This switches on the electronic circuits, and the gyroscope inside the missile is spun up to operating speed, after which a gas generator in the rear of the missile launches it from the

tube. As it clears the tube the thre fins unfold, and these are canted s that they give the missile a slow rol

Missile propulsion

Almost immediately the first of th 60 rockets fires; each rocket is contro led by the gyroscope and the missile roll, so that whichever rocket happer to be beneath the missile at the time ignited, and it thrusts the missile u and forward. As its effect begins to d away the gyro selects the next rock at the 6 o'clock position and fires i and this continues, rocket after rock being fire to give a series of impulse and keep the missile flying.

The infra-red flare in the tail of th missile was ignited at launch, and th

telescopic sight

tracker unit

error sensor

electronic assembly

tracker support

launch tube

support stand

tracker unit lens cover

aft end cap

is now seen in the sight. but the operator takes no notice; all he has to do is keep the crosswires of his sight aligned with his target. An infra-red detector in the sight registers the tail flare image and automatically measures its displacement from the centre of the crosswires, which is a measure of the missile's deviation from the ideal trajectory to the target.

Having made the measurement, a micro-computer calculates what correction to the missile's flight is necessary, and it transmits this correction down the wire that is unreeling behind the missile. This correction is processed by the circuits in the missile, and one of the 60 rockets is fired — not when it is at 6 o'clock, but when it

is on the side from which thrust is needed to push the missile into alignment with the sight.

Corrective blasts

So if a pure right-to-left movement is needed, then a rocket would fire at the 3 o'clock position; if some upward movement was needed too, then the electronics and the gyro between them might fire a rocket at, say, the 4 o'clock position. The missile responds; the sight examines it, decides on a correction, and fires another rocket; and so it goes on, constantly firing rockets to promote forward movement and also periodically firing them to produce trajectory corrections.

The optical sighting unit has stadia lines covering a 6-metre area at 1,000 metres, so as soon as an approaching tank fills the sight picture you know it is within range.

Given a good operator, Dragon has a reasonable chance of hitting and stopping a tank. Given a poor operator, there are problems. If the operator fails to hold a steady aim and lets it wander off and then come back, the side rockets are worked overtime in order to generate corrections, and it is not unheard of for a missile to run out

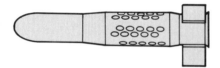

When firing at moving targets you must remember that Dragon travels at 100 metres per second, and a fast-moving enemy vehicle may be moving at about 10 metres per second. The enemy may have time to move into nearby cover and you will have wasted a missile and revealed your position unnecessarily.

of rockets before it gets to the target whereupon it simply runs out o steam and ploughs into the ground To be fair, though, this is an extrem case and only happens with traine operators.

However, there is no doubt tha Dragon is not as effective as had bee hoped and is not as good as, say Milan. The principal drawback seem to be its slow speed, which is due t the unusual method of propulsion and steering. This restricts the max imum range and also allows a targe some fair amount of movement durin the flight, which means it has to b tracked by the operator, which mean that more rockets are going to be

Battlefield Evaluation: comparing

Dragon

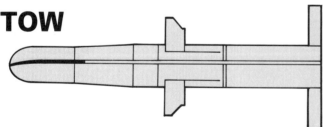

Specification:
Missile weight: 6.2 kg
Launcher weight: 7.6 kg
Warhead: 2.45 kg
Minimum range: 75 m
Maximum range: 1000 m
Armour penetration: 400 mm

Dragon's main problem is that its unique propulsion and steering system makes it slow and short-ranged. Milan can reach 2000 metres in 13 seconds, whereas Dragon takes 10 seconds to reach its maximum range of 1000 metres. Slow speed gives an enemy tank a chance to drive behind a tree or other obstacle, which could set off the missile or snag the control wire. It also gives the enemy a better chance of suppressing the operator by spotting his position and opening fire with everything they have.

Assessment
Reliability	★★★
Accuracy	★★
Age	★★★
Worldwide users	★★★

If Dragon's performance cannot be substantially increased, the US Army will have to find a replacement.

TOW

Specification:
Missile weight: 28 kg
Launcher weight: 93 kg
Warhead: 5.9 kg
Minimum range: 65 m
Maximum range: 3750 m
Armour penetration: 800 mm+

TOW entered service in 1970, five years earlier than Dragon, and has proved far more successful. It is simple to operate, has a very long range and the same missile can be fired from ground and helicopter mountings. It flies at 200 metres per second and carries a very powerful warhead. However, it needs a four-man crew for action in the ground role and this, plus its size and weight, aakes it more suitable as a vehicle mounted weapon.

Assessment
Reliability	★★★★
Accuracy	★★★★
Age	★★
Worldwide users	★★★★

TOW's position is safe: its warhead can still defeat any Main Battle Tank in service.

Milan

Specification:
Missile weight: 11.3 kg
Launcher weight: 6.4 kg
Warhead: 1.45 kg shaped-charge high explosive
Minimum range: 25 m
Maximum range: 2000 m
Armour penetration: 1000 mm+

Thanks to the new missile warhead introduced in 1984, Milan is able to defeat over a metre of heavy tank armour plate. It would make sense for the US Army to use the same weapon as its NATO allies, but whether they will abandon Dragon in favour of Milan remains a matter for speculation. All armies await the arrival of 'fire and forget' anti-tank missiles, which can guide themselves onto the target without any assistance from the operator.

Assessment
Reliability	★★★★
Accuracy	★★★★★
Age	★★
Worldwide users	★★

If Dragon cannot be improved it would make a lot of sense for the US Army to adopt Milan instead.

urned in altering course. There have
een various 'Product Improvement'
rogrammes suggested for Dragon,
ut short of a complete redesign these
re merely tinkering and cannot pro-
uce any radical changes in perform-
nce.

At the moment there is a good deal
f argument going on as to whether
Dragon should be expensively over-
auled or whether it would be cheap-
r and easier to stop production, let it
vaste out, and replace it with Milan.
This would double the engagement
ange, considerably increase the hit
robability figure, and have the added
onus of bringing the USA into line
vith most of the remainder of NATO.

The propulsion system

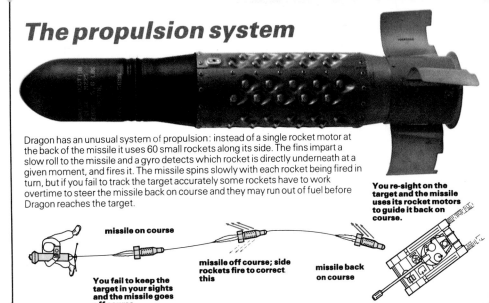

Dragon has an unusual system of propulsion: instead of a single rocket motor at the back of the missile it uses 60 small rockets along its side. The fins impart a slow roll to the missile and a gyro detects which rocket is directly underneath at a given moment, and fires it. The missile spins slowly with each rocket being fired in turn, but if you fail to track the target accurately some rockets have to work overtime to steer the missile back on course and they may run out of fuel before Dragon reaches the target.

You re-sight on the target and the missile uses its rocket motors to guide it back on course.

missile on course

You fail to keep the target in your sights and the missile goes off course

missile off course; side rockets fire to correct this

missile back on course

the Dragon with its rivals

AT-4 'Spigot'

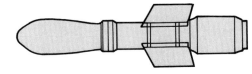

'Spigot' is the NATO reporting name for this Soviet anti-tank missile, which may be known to them as 'Fagot'. Almost certainly a copy of Milan, the result of successful espionage, it substantially improves the anti-tank capability of Warsaw Pact forces. The sight is smaller than that of Milan and the computer system is in a box under the launch rail, which may give it a slightly lower silhouette in the firing position.

Specification:
Missile weight: not known
Launcher weight: 40 kg including missile
Warhead: slightly heavier than Milan
Minimum range: not known
Maximum range: 2000 m +
Armour penetration: not known

Assessment
Reliability ⋆⋆⋆
Accuracy ⋆⋆⋆
Age ⋆
Worldwide users ⋆⋆⋆

AT-4 'Spigot' is a copy of Milan, produced after the Soviets 'acquired' enough technical information.

Carl Gustav

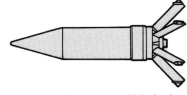

The British medium anti-tank weapon for many years, this is shortly to be replaced by LAW80. It is a simple recoilless gun and it fires an 84-mm HEAT round, which can hit stationary vehicles at up to 500 metres and moving ones within 400 metres. Bofors, who manufacture Carl Gustav, have now produced an improved model firing rocket-assisted projectiles that offer a 50 per cent improvement in effective range and increased armour penetration.

Specification: (FFV 550 improved Carl Gustav)
Missile weight: 3 kg
Launcher weight: 15 kg
Warhead: 2.2 kg
Minimum range: point blank
Maximum range: 700 m
Armour penetration: 400 mm+

Assessment
Reliability ⋆⋆⋆⋆⋆
Accuracy ⋆⋆⋆
Age ⋆
Worldwide users ⋆

Carl Gustav is typical of the large recoilless weapons which are the alternative to ATGWs.

Folgore

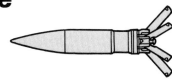

Similar to Carl Gustav, Folgore offers an alternative to the incredibly expensive guided anti-tank missiles or could be used to bridge the gap between close-range infantry anti-tank rockets and long-range weapons like TOW. Produced by the Italian firm of Breda, Folgore fires a rocket-assisted projectile from a 1.85-metre long tube which can be rested on your shoulder or mounted on a tripod. When tripod-mounted, it uses an optical-electronic system to estimate target range, speed and calculate elevation.

Specification:
Missile weight: 5.2 kg
Launcher weight: 19 kg
Warhead: 3 kg
Minimum range: point blank
Maximum range: 700 m
Armour penetration: 400 mm+

Assessment
Reliability ⋆⋆⋆⋆⋆
Accuracy ⋆⋆⋆
Age ⋆
Worldwide users ⋆

Folgore is far cheaper than Dragon but only marginally less effective at close range.

Mixing it with the M16

There is an old saying that if you ask the right question you are half-way to getting the right answer. But there are occasions when you can ask the wrong questions and still get the right answer: the history of the M16 rifle is a case in point. In 1948 the US Army set up the Operations Research Office (ORO), intending to use scientific analysis to help in the design of future equipment. One of their first tasks was to look at the design of body armour, and to do this they began studying the nature of battle casualties.

Dispersed bullets

This led them to believe that rifle bullet wounds were just as random as shell splinter wounds, and from this, in 1952, they produced a secret paper called 'Operational Requirements for an Infantry Hand Weapon'. This, among other things, argued that insistence on aimed fire was a waste of time and that a small-calibre weapon firing a dispersed burst of bullets would stand a better chance of incapacitating an enemy at the short ranges at which rifles were fired in combat.

Thus the Salvo programe was born,

The M16 family

The M16 family has grown into a complete weapons system, including light machine-guns and carbines.

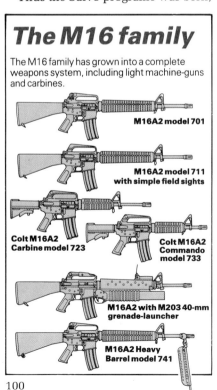

M16A2 model 701

M16A2 model 711 with simple field sights

Colt M16A2 Carbine model 723

Colt M16A2 Commando model 733

M16A2 with M203 40-mm grenade-launcher

M16A2 Heavy Barrel model 741

The M16 appeared in Vietnam with some of the first contingents of US troops to arrive there, and later became the standard US service rifle. Short and incredibly light, it proved an ideal weapon for jungle warfare as long as it was properly maintained.

resulting in cartridges with multiple bullets, flechettes and several other ambitious and exotic ideas. As a result of the Salvo investigations the Army decided to press for .22 calibre military rifle. Several of the experimental Salvo weapons had used the Remington . The Army believed that a simple rifle firing a small bullet, and therefore easily controlled in automatic fire, would be preferable to the traditional heavy rifle firing 7.62 mm bullets.

The Army turned to Armalite, who had started developing a new rifle in the early 1950s when George Sullivan, a California patent lawyer, began wondering whether modern materials such as plastics and alloys might be useful in a new generation of weapons. He was joined by Eugene Stoner, a man with some experience of weapons design, and the financing was provided by Fairchild.

Altered Remington

By 1956 they had produced a 7.62-mm weapon, the AR-10, and they then turned to the .222 calibre. The original Remington cartridge was

With practically no recoil, the M16 is a very comfortable weapon to shoot; you can keep the sights on the target even when shooting rapidly.

Firing the AR-10, the father of the M16 rifle and one of the first to be designed from the start as an assault rifle: it is light, but absorbs the recoil very well.

You cock the M16 by pulling back the charging handle, located just behind the carrying handle. If the magazine is empty the bolt carrier will be held to the rear.

A US Army Ranger carries the Colt Commander. This was a cut-down M16 developed during the Vietnam war for close-quarter fighting. Barrel length is halved, which forces you to fit a large suppressor or produce horrendous muzzle flash.

Inside the M16

The M16 is gas-operated, but whereas most such weapons use the gases produced on firing to move a piston which in turn moves the bolt, the gases in the M16 act directly on the bolt. This is a simpler system, but it won't work properly unless the weapon is regularly cleaned.

Front sight

Gas port

Gas pipe

Handguard
This is the most obvious difference between the M16A1 and M16A2: the handguard on the latter has pronounced vertical ribs for improved grip.

Flash suppressor

Forward sling swivel

An M16 rests on an American 'Tiger Stripe' camouflage jacket, a favourite uniform of the US Special Forces in Vietnam. Professional troops had few troubles with the M16 in Vietnam, but freshly-drafted conscripts who didn't clean their rifles had endless stoppages.

somewhat altered in an attempt to reach the ballistics demanded by the Army; the AR-10 rifle was scaled down; and the result was known as the AR-15 in .223 calibre. But in 1959 the Army lost interest in the idea and turned instead to a new development programme, the 6-mm SPIW (Special Purpose Individual Weapon).

Air Force requirement

That might have been the end of the story but for the US Air Force, who were looking for a small and handy short-range weapon with which to arm airfield guards. They looked at the AR-15, liked it, and ordered 8,000 in 1962. Shortly after this it was issued to guards in Vietnam. The ARVN (Army of the Republic of Vietnam) saw them, thought that they

Stripping the M16

1 Push in the takedown pin with a bullet after locking the bolt open, placing the fire selector on safe and checking that the receiver and chamber are clear.

2 Pivot the upper receiver from the lower receiver. These can be separated by pushing the receiver pivot pin forward of the magazine housing, but this is not necessary for a basic strip.

3 Pull back the charging handle and the bolt carrier.

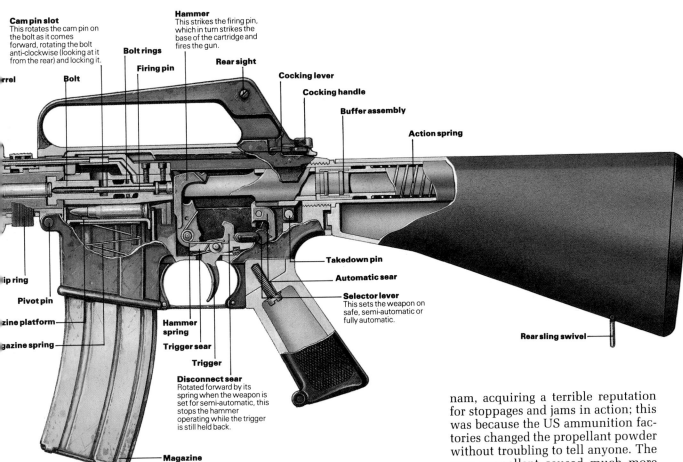

Cam pin slot
This rotates the cam pin on the bolt as it comes forward, rotating the bolt anti-clockwise (looking at it from the rear) and locking it.

Bolt rings

Firing pin

Bolt

Hammer
This strikes the firing pin, which in turn strikes the base of the cartridge and fires the gun.

Rear sight

Cocking lever

Cocking handle

Buffer assembly

Action spring

rrel

ip ring

Pivot pin

zine platform

gazine spring

Hammer spring

Trigger sear

Trigger

Disconnect sear
Rotated forward by its spring when the weapon is set for semi-automatic, this stops the hammer operating while the trigger is still held back.

Takedown pin

Automatic sear

Selector lever
This sets the weapon on safe, semi-automatic or fully automatic.

Rear sling swivel

Magazine

would be ideal for their small-statured men, and asked for some to be supplied by the USA. One thousand were sent out in 1962, and it became highly popular.

The US Army decided to get in on the act; the 6-mm SPIW programme was a failure, and interest returned to the AR-15. In 1963 85,000 rifles were ordered for the Army and another 19,000 for the Air Force.

Before the Army could standardize the weapon, they insisted on some small modifications; of these, the most important was the addition of a 'bolt closing device'. Occasionally a dirty cartridge or a dirty chamber caused the breech to stick before being fully closed, and a positive closing plunger was added on the right hand side of the receiver. With this, the rifle now became the M16A1 and received official blessing.

It got a semi-official cursing in Viet-

nam, acquiring a terrible reputation for stoppages and jams in action; this was because the US ammunition factories changed the propellant powder without troubling to tell anyone. The new propellant caused much more fouling, compounded by idleness on the part of soldiers who didn't bother to clean the rifle.

Piping the gas

The reason the powder caused problems was tied in with the peculiar method of operation of the M16. Most gas-operated weapons tap gas from the barrel into a cylinder, where it drives a piston backwards to operate the bolt. But the M16 simplified things by simply piping the gas back and allowing it to hit the bolt carrier and, literally, blast it back.

4 Remove the bolt carrier and the bolt. If the weapon is very dirty, remove the extractor pin and the extractor for cleaning.

5 The cleaning kit lives in the hollow butt. Because of the way that the gas operates directly on the bolt, it is especially important to keep the M16 clean.

6 When cleaning the bolt, check it for any cracks or fractures, particularly around the cam pin area. Replace the bolt if it is pitted near the firing pin hole.

The carrier moved backwards and curved slot, holding a lug on the bolt caused the bolt to revolve and unlock from the chamber, after which the carrier pulled the bolt back and ejected the spent case. Two springs then propelled the bolt forward again to collect a new round from the magazine and re-load.

Foul gas

During the backward stroke a hammer had been cocked, and a fresh pull on the trigger now fired the next

The US Army is now re-equipping with the M16A2. The version it has adopted fires either single-shot or three-round bursts; it cannot fire fully automatic.

Battlefield Evaluation: comparing

M16A2

Specification:
Cartridge: 5.56 mm NATO
Weight: 3.85 kg
Length: (overall) 1000 mm
Barrel length: 508 mm
Cyclic rate of fire: 600 rounds per minute
Magazine: 20 or 30 round box

The M16A2, adopted by the US Army in 1985, incorporates a number of changes to the M16A1: the barrel is slightly stronger, the handguard re-shaped, and the barrel rifling altered to suit the NATO's new 5.56-mm cartridge. The US Army's M16A2s have a three-round burst option instead of full auto, in the belief that automatic fire is a waste of ammunition.

Assessment
Reliability	★★★★
Accuracy	★★★
Age	★
Worldwide users	★★★

The M16 can be fired left-handed without difficulty: particularly handy in urban combat.

Heckler & Koch G41

Specification:
Cartridge: 5.56 mm × 45
Weight: 4.1 kg
Length: (overall) 997 mm
Barrel length: 450 mm
Cyclic rate of fire: 850 rounds per minute
Magazine: 30-round box

Based on the G3 rifle, the Heckler & Koch G41 was specifically developed to fire the standard NATO 5.56-mm cartridge. It can accept the M16 magazine (now a requirement for all NATO rifles), gives three-round bursts or fully automatic fire, and has a built-in telescopic mount. Although new, it is already in service with one unnamed country and is being tested by others.

Assessment
Reliability	★★★★
Accuracy	★★★★
Age	★
Worldwide users	★

Heckler & Koch have designed the G41 around the new NATO standard 5.56-mm × 45 cartridge.

Fabrique National FNC

Specification:
Cartridge: 5.56 mm × 45 (M193 or SS109)
Weight: 3.8 kg
Length: (overall) 997 mm
Barrel length: 449 mm
Cyclic rate of fire: 600-700 rounds per minute
Magazine: 30-round box

Fabrique National are well known for their FN FAL 7.62-mm rifle, known to the British Army as the SLR or L1A1, and the FNC is their response to the trend towards 5.56-mm weapons. It is gas-operated, with a piston and cylinder above the barrel, and uses a rotating bolt. It also gives the choice of three-round bursts or automatic fire, and has so far been adopted by Sweden and Indonesia.

Assessment
Reliability	★★★
Accuracy	★★★
Age	★
Worldwide users	★

The FNC follows the basic layout of the famous FN FAL, but fires either the SS109 or M193 5.56-mm cartridges.

ound. Automatic fire was achieved by the bolt carrier tripping the sear as the bolt finally closed, and so squirting the bolt carrier full of fouling-laden gas was bound to cause problems. Some education of the troops, prolific issue of cleaning kit, and modification to the propellant cleared up that problem, and since then the M16 has been trouble-free.

Minor improvements

In 1985 the M16A2 was approved. This tidied up one or two minor details which experience had shown needed attention. The flash hider, for example, had a slot in the bottom which allowed gas to blast down from the muzzle and kick up dust, revealing your position and obscuring your view; so this slot has been done away with.

The American Army started by trying to find a weapon which would do the job without needing any skill from the man holding it; they asked the wrong question. What they have finished up with is an accurate and reliable rifle which is virtually the world standard in its calibre; they got the right answer.

'Out here on the perimeter there are no stars': a US Marine sentry in Vietnam. The vast numbers of M16s captured when South Vietnam fell to the Communists have turned up all over the world.

the M16 with its rivals

Steyr AUG

The Austrian company of Steyr's Army Universal Gun has proved increasingly popular since its introducton in 1976. The plastic magazine is transparent, so that you can see how many rounds remain, and is tougher than most metal magazines. It was just beaten the M16 for adoption by the Australian and New Zealand armies, and you may be sure that this will influence other armies in the future.

Specification:
Cartridge: 5.56 mm × 45
Weight: 4.1 kg
Length: (overall) 790 mm
Barrel length: 508 mm
Cyclic rate of fire: 650 rounds per minute
Magazine: 30-round box

Assessment
Reliability	****
Accuracy	***
Age	**
Worldwide users	**

The ultra-modern Steyr has recently beaten the M16 to become the new Australian Army rifle.

Beretta AR70

Beretta produced the AR70 after closely studying existing 5.56-mm rifles, especially the M16. It is a straightforward, conventional weapon with few frills, carefully designed to minimise the amount of dirt that can enter the weapon. Capable of semi- and fully-automatic fire, its only problem is that the cocking handle is the only part connecting piston to bolt carrier: lose it and you have an unusable firearm.

Specification:
Cartridge: 5.56 mm × 45 (M193 or SS109)
Weight: 4.1 kg
Length: (overall) 955 mm
Barrel length: 450 mm
Cyclic rate of fire: 650 rounds per minute
Magazine: 30-round box

Assessment
Reliability	***
Accuracy	***
Age	*
Worldwide users	*

The Beretta AR70 and all its accessories: this has been adopted by Italian Special Forces.

SAR 80

This is produced by Chartered Industries of Singapore, a company founded in 1967 to manufacture the M16 under licence. It was designed by the British company of Sterling Armament and had to be at least as good as the M16, but possible to build very cheaply with the latest production techniques. The result is a basic, gas-piston operated assault rifle with an attractive price tag.

Specification:
Cartridge: 5.56 mm (US M193 or M196)
Weight: 3.7 kg (unloaded)
Length: (overall) 970 mm
Barrel length: 459 mm
Cyclic rate of fire: 600-850 rounds per minute
Magazine: 20- or 30-round box

Assessment
Reliability	***
Accuracy	***
Age	*
Worldwide users	*

The SAR80 follows the M16 tradition of a lightweight rifle suited to smaller Asian soldiers.

The Search for Water

Water is a basic human need. There is no adequate substitute, and without it you cannot live more than a few days. Within the human body water acts as a stabilizer; it helps to maintain warmth in cold environments, and is vital to staying cool in hot environments. It is also part of the body's mechanism for distributing food and removing waste. As soon as you are cut off from a source of fresh water, you begin to dehydrate.

The rate at which you dehydrate depends on a number of factors: the amount of water your body already contains, the clothing you are wearing, the local temperature, how hard you are working, whether you are in shade or sunlight, whether you are smoking and whether you are calm or nervous.

If you allow dehydration to continue, there will come a point when you can no longer search for water. Your first priority is to minimise further dehydration and, having done this, you must find water. (If you are stranded in a desert with little chance of finding water, stay still to prevent further dehydration, and make effort to signal for rescue.)

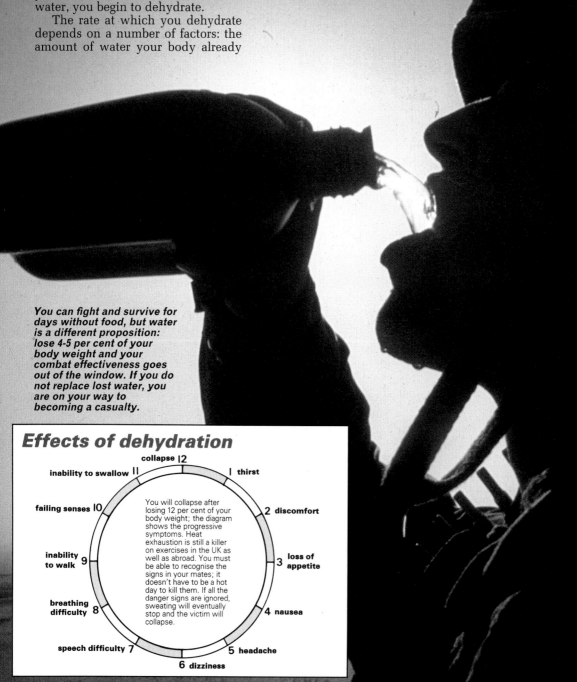

You can fight and survive for days without food, but water is a different proposition: lose 4-5 per cent of your body weight and your combat effectiveness goes out of the window. If you do not replace lost water, you are on your way to becoming a casualty.

Effects of dehydration

collapse 12
inability to swallow 11 — 1 thirst
failing senses 10 — 2 discomfort
inability to walk 9 — 3 loss of appetite
breathing difficulty 8 — 4 nausea
speech difficulty 7 — 5 headache
6 dizziness

You will collapse after losing 12 per cent of your body weight; the diagram shows the progressive symptoms. Heat exhaustion is still a killer on exercises in the UK as well as abroad. You must be able to recognise the signs in your mates; it doesn't have to be a hot day to kill them. If all the danger signs are ignored, sweating will eventually stop and the victim will collapse.

Points for Survival

1 Avoid eating until you have secured a source of safe water.
2 Do not ration your water; drink as much as you can when you can.
3 Urine is a good indicator of dehydration. The darker its colour, the more dehydrated you are.
4 Bacteria multiplies faster in warm water, so water gathered early in the morning, at its coolest, is safer.
5 To reduce dehydration:
★Find shade
★Move slowly and do not smoke
★Cover exposed skin to prevent evaporation of sweat
★Suck a pebble (helps prevent exhalation of moisture through the mouth)

Water can often be found in the hollows of trees, but is usually tainted with tannin from the bark. If you expect rain, empty the hollow out, wait until it fills up and then boil the new water.

Finding water

You do not have to be in a desert to have difficulty finding water. Forests often offer such poor visibility that, although surrounded by water-loving trees, you cannot spot readily-available surface water. (In combat conditions, however, you may have to deliberately avoid obvious sources of water, for fear of ambush.)

So how do you go about finding water? The first thing you do is to remember the following points:

Water runs downhill, so make for lower country.

Where there is water, there is usually an abundance of lush vegetation. If possible, learn to recognise the moisture-loving plants in the area. If this vegetation is wilted or dead, it probably indicates chemical pollution.

Animals need water too. Observe the habits of the local wildlife; it may lead you to a source of water.

Grain- and seed-eating birds need water, so observe them too.

Listen for frogs croaking: they live in water.

Cliffs often have seepages of water at their base, so look carefully.

Sources of water (assuming no equipment)

Familiarise yourself with the various sources of water and their relative merits.

Dew

Dew is one of the most reliable sources of water for the survivor. It can be collected soon after it has started to form until it evaporates in the morning sunlight. Improvise a mop from an absorbent article of clothing. Drag this through long grass or use it to wipe the condensed moisture from shrubs and rocks. If you do not have a convenient mop, finely teased, non-poisonous inner barks or grasses can be used. When the mop is saturated, wring out the water into a container. Although labour-intensive, this is a very effective way to collect water.

Dew itself is a pure source of water, but when you wipe it off vegetation and rocks you also wipe off bacteria and perhaps parasites. It is therefore best to boil this water before consumption.

2 Rain and snow

Rainwater is usually the safest source of water in the wilderness. If it rains, make sure you gather as much as you can. But remember the water is

Most soldiers take water for granted. In British forces, steps are being taken to recognise water as an important factor by forming trained water 'recce' teams and introducing strict controls – for instance, not being allowed to drink without permission.

Iranian prisoners receive a drink from an Iraqi recce unit atop a BRDM-2. In a protracted campaign, shortage of water may well be a reason for not taking prisoners.

only as pure as your method of collection: if you are in doubt, boil it before consumption. Snow, if it is clean, is probably pure. The major problem with snow is melting it: a time-consuming and labour-intensive process, as you require eight to 10 containers of snow to produce one container of water.

3 Ice

Ice is not pure and should always be boiled before consumption, but is far more economical as a source of water than snow. Icicles are often found hanging from trees and rocks, so may provide you with a ready source of water. Those hanging from trees may be slightly stained brown by the tannin in the bark, but unless they

are very heavily stained they will be safe to drink after boiling.

4 Puddles and hidden water

Rainwater is often found trapped in depressions in rocks, called kettles, and in puddles. While such water may smell foul and be stagnant, it only needs filtering and boiling to make it drinkable.

Rainwater can also often be found trapped in hollows in trees. Unfortunately, this is often so badly polluted with tannin that it is undrinkable. However, if you expect rain you can bale these hollows out and let them fill with fresh rainwater; as long as you use the water before it too becomes tannin-stained, you have a handy water tank. Always boil this water before drinking it, and only use water found in non-poisonous trees.

Note: Tannin-stained water, although undrinkable, can be boiled to make a very effective antiseptic: unlike syn-

Tree ice
Remember, you will need to boil it. On a chemical battlefield, however, this would be useless.

Birch sap
A North American Indian technique is to tap of the sap as shown, with a collecting barrel attached to the tap. Be careful that you do not completely break the tree's ring of bark when doing this several times.

Mud pool (above)
Not instantly recognisable as a source of wate but if you filter and boil it you can drink it.

Stagnant water (left)
This can also provide drinking water and in many situations this will be the only type of water available. Treatment of water is covered in STONE AGE SURVIVAL No. 2.

hetic antiseptics, tannin actually promotes healing. You can also dilute it to a mild tea and drink it to ease diarrhoea.

5 Drinkable saps

For short-term relief of thirst, you may be able to tap the sap of certain trees. The sap of maple, birch and sycamore can be tapped during the early spring (sycamore will produce sap from spring to autumn, depending on local conditions). Sap is thirst-quenching but it contains sugar, which if taken in sufficient quantity will hasten dehydration; in fact, the woodland North American Indians still boil maple and birch sap to produce sugar.

Only mature trees should be tapped, and the sap drunk while fresh, as it will ferment if stored. Some plants can also be used to provide water.

6 Springs and seepages

Springs are often regarded as fool-proof sources of drinking water, but unfortunately this is not true: spring water should always be boiled before drinking. Very often, springs are covered with soil and appear as patches of saturated ground supporting lush plant growth. To obtain water from these areas, dig an Indian Well.

7 Ponds

These are principally a feature of farmland, and are therefore a potential source of water for the evading soldier. Such water should always be considered suspect, as at the very least there will be fluke infestation. Keep contact with this water to a minimum, and if used as a source of drinking water, filter and thoroughly boil it before drinking.

8 Streams, rivers and lakes

Streams are often a tempting source of water, but care should be taken as they are very often polluted by decaying carcasses of animals that have drowned or become caught in boggy ground. In alpine regions, the clear, ice-cold glacial meltwaters carry an invisible hazard: sediment – rock powder scoured from living rock by the awesome power of the glacier. If this is not filtered out, you may get digestive problems.

The further water travels from its source, the more pollutants it picks up. In an age where chemicals are an integral part of farming and land management, rivers and lakes should be avoided as sources of water.

Indian Well

The Indian Well is an easily prepared and efficient method of collecting reasonably good water. Selection of the ground is all-important and the water produced requires filtering and boiling. Also, it takes some time to produce clear water, and quality is dependent on soil type. In practice, watch out for sources of contamination, boil very carefully, and add Steritabs.

Choose an area of saturated ground. If in a tactical environment, don't pick a place that can be easily spotted.

If you haven't a bowl for baling out (see STONE AGE SURVIVAL No. 2), cupped hands will do.

This is good enough to use; the water seeping into the well has a filtering effect. The water will get cleaner the longer you spend baling out.

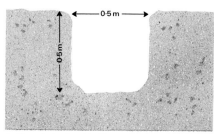

1 Dig a hole about half a metre deep and half a metre wide. Water will begin to seep into the hole.

2 You can push a stick into the sides of the well to increase seepage of water into the well.

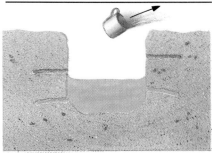

3 Bale out this water carefully so that you do not stir up the sediment at the bottom of the hole. Repeat this process until the seeping water is fairly clear.

4 After some time, the water at the top of the well will be clear enough to collect. Be careful not to disturb the muddy layer that usually lurks at the bottom.

Purifying Water

Now you've found a source of water. Is it safe to drink? The answer seems obvious — assume the water is dirty and purify it. But dehydration is causing you to be uncharacteristically impatient and irritable. You are tired, hungry, lonely and somewhat frightened. Your hands and shins are covered in the scratches you sustained searching what seemed like every patch of vegetation in the last 100 miles. And but for the incessant biting of the mosquitoes you would fall asleep.

You are faced with water that will need filtering and boiling before it is safe to drink, but you have no container and no fire. Surely one little sip won't hurt?

The hazard of polluted water

Without the support of modern medicine to fall back on, wilderness survival is all about maintaining good health. The human body is an amazing machine, but it is finely tuned: it only takes one drop of contaminated water to make you ill.

Of the many waterborne problems you may develop, the most common is diarrhoea. In a survival situation, diarrhoea may prove fatal. It causes dehydration and makes hygiene very difficult, increasing the risk of further unpleasant infections, and destroys the will to live.

To make your water safe, you will need three things:
1 Fire
2 A container
3 A filter

As a fire will also warm you, drive away the mosquitoes and boost your morale, it is usually best to start this first. Hopefully you will have practised your firelighting skill, as this is a bad time to learn!

Improvised water containers

Improvised water containers fall into three categories:
1 Kettles: containers that can be used directly over flames
2 Cauldrons: cannot be used directly over flames, but can be used for rock boiling
3 Storage: containers that are solely for carrying or storing safe water

Above, right and below: Cherry or birch bark bowls can be made by simple folding, and improved by stitching; the more robust version is shown here stitched and with a wooden rim. You will have to soak the bark for a long time.

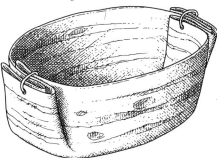

Kettles

Kettles can be made from flammable materials because the water contained within them prevents their burning. The secret is not to allow the flames to reach beyond the water level.

1 Bamboo

In some tropical regions, bamboo can be found with stems large enough to be turned into kettles. Many other containers can also be improvised from bamboo, and sometimes fresh drinking water can be found trapped in the stems.

Birch or cherry bark

he woodland Indians of North
merica routinely made kettles from
irch bark while on their travels. Only
e outer bark is used. It should be
arefully removed from an unblem-
shed section of the trunk, and can be
ade pliable by either soaking or
ently warming by the fire. The brown
side of the bark is the most durable
de, and is used to form the outside of
ntainers which are simply made by
lding.

Cauldrons

Cauldrons are made from materials
at will hold water but are not suit-
ble for direct heating; put heated
cks into the water to boil it.

If your local soil is clay or clay-like
nough to contain muddy water, a
round cauldron can be made. Dig a
owl-shaped depression in the
round and smooth the inside. Form a
ised rim at the top, to help prevent
umus falling into the cauldron.

Make the cauldron one third larger
an the amount of water you intend
boil. This will allow for the water
isplaced by the heated rocks. To pre-
ent sediment muddying your water,
ou will need to line the pit. For this
ou can use either some material, (for
xample, a T-shirt) or large non-
oisonous leaves such as dock or bur-
ock. Take great care to ensure that
e lining fits snugly.

The water purified in this type of
auldron will always be a little
uddy, but if you leave it to settle you
an skim clear water off of the top.

Natural cauldrons
Rocks and trees

Water can often be found in depres-
ions in rocks, and the hollows in
ees, and these can be turned into
eady-made cauldrons. Again, allow
r the displacement of the heated
cks by choosing a depression large
nough. If possible, it is best to scrape
ny slime out of these depressions
rior to their use. This is especially
nportant when using tree hollows.
emember, never rock boil in a
oisonous tree.

Skin

If you are able to catch an animal of
e size of a rabbit upwards, you will
ave secured meat as well as two con-
ainers good enough to stew it in: if
ou are careful with the skinning and
utting, both the skin and the stomach
an be used as cauldrons.

To use the skin you can leave the fur
n or take it off, as you please. To use
e stomach it is best turned inside
ut. You have a choice when making

Bowl burning

Wooden bowls and containers have been used for centuries and are well within your capabilities to
produce. The method is called 'burn and scrape'. First, select a piece of wood of the right thickness.
Remember the hardwoods are by nature a lot harder to work, but the product is more durable.
Softer dead woods are usually easier.

1 Select a few choice
embers from your fire
and place them in the
centre of the log. Hold
them in place with a
twig and blow through a
tube if possible, perhaps
a reed straw. The
embers will flare and
char the wood.

2 Once a sufficient area
has been charred,
remove the embers and
scrape out the charred
wood with a knife or
sharp stone. Do not burn
too fast or the wood
might crack.

3 Repeat the process. It
becomes easier as the
hole gets deeper at each
stage, so you don't need
to hold the embers in
place. Don't blow too
hard – just steadily
enough to keep the
embers going.

4 The vital ingredient is
patience; this method
does take time, but you
will have a lasting piece
of equipment. The bowl
on the left is made from
a knot in the trunk of the
tree.

your skin cauldron. You can line a pit with it, securing it around the rim by stakes, or you can suspend it from a tripod.

3 Wooden bowls

Bowls and containers can be carved out of wood. While not as quickly constructed as the previous methods, wooden bowls are well within the capabilities of a survivor. If carefully made, they are portable and very durable.

The best method of producing a wooden bowl is to 'burn and scrape'. To achieve this, make a small depression in the centre of your bowl-to-be and place a couple of glowing coals in this depression. By then blowing on the coals, ideally through a reed straw, you can use them to char the surrounding wood.

When you have charred a patch of wood, scrape it away using a sharp stone, and begin the process again. It does not take long to form a reasonable sized bowl.

Storage containers

The manufacture of storage containers is a long-term prospect. They can be made from the materials discussed above, and also from clay pottery and tightly-woven basketry.

Filtering

Having secured a container in which to boil your water, you now need a filter to remove the particles of dirt suspended in the water.

Improvised filter

The simplest filter that can be improvised uses a pair of ordinary trousers. Simply turn them inside out, placing one leg inside the other, and tie the leg off at the bottom. Soak the material before use: this helps tighten the weave, making the filter more efficient. Suspend the filter so that you can easily fill it, with the container positioned underneath to collect the clean water that drips out. Such filters can be improved by filling them with charcoal (not ash, which would produce a strong lye solution).

Rock boiling

Rock boiling is an easy and effective way to purify water. The rocks must be of a manageable size and weight, and thoroughly dry. (Rocks from stream beds and damp places contain moisture which, when heated, expands, causing the rock to explode. Also, glass-like rocks such as flint and obsidian should be avoided.)

Heat the rocks in your fire, and when hot transfer them to your container with some improvised tongs. Tap off any ash before dropping them in the water.

Do not wait to use these skills until you have to. Practice is essential to success.

NB When practising, only gather bark from dead trees.

A simple water filter

If you are going to be operating in an area for some time, this sort of filter will save you a good deal of time: if there is no risk of discovery, you can leave it set up and on the go while you carry on with other tasks.

A spare pair of lightweight issue trousers or, even better, combat trousers with the liners in, make excellent filters because of their dense weave. Soak them thoroughly before you start. A vast improvement is the addition of charcoal: for a small filter you can use spare S6 respirator canisters tied to the bottom of the bag (they contain animated charcoal). Make sure you are not going to need them for their original purpose as they are useless when wet!

charcoal

double thickness of material

filtered water (filtrate)

After filtering to make water safe to (you need to boil it. This can be done fireproof containers in the following v using heated rocks. You need a fire; thick, reasonably straight branches c length for the stand and cross braces green wood for fire tongs; and an an skin, fresh or cured (if fresh, make su get all the fat off). Rabbit skins are to – you really need large hare size and for a worthwhile set-up.

1 Once you have got a decent fire go build a platform of sticks on the fire, layers at 90° to each other, to put the on. While these are heating up you ca the finishing touches to the stand.

2 Pour your filtered water into the sk not overfill it, or you will lose precious when you add the rocks. When the r have heated up, pick them up using g twigs.

3 Carefully put the rocks into the wa Note that the feet of the animal are le the skin as they make useful anchor

4 Continue adding rocks until the water boils. You can repeat the process by replacing 'used rocks' back on the fire.

5 This is also a good method for cooking without containers: you can make soups or stews by putting the ingredients into the water with the hot rocks.

6 The stand and skin container set up. Disaster can occur if you try to pour your filtered water in too quickly. Push your hand into the skin to form a bowl and pour the water in slowly; this will allow the skin to expand and take the water.

Fighting Fit

SELECTION

THE RUSSIAN SPECIAL FORCES

Airborne troops race out of the latest version of the Mi-8 'Hip' assault helicopter. Spetsnaz 'snatch squads' were in action last winter against the Mujahideen, trying to capture American Stinger or British Blowpipe SAMs. Note the folding-stock AK-74s and the heavy rocket armament of the HIP.

Mobilised at short notice, to penetrate a defence base, troops are parachuted at night into a desolate region — such as Siberia — and are pursued by motorised infantry over vast distances. But the target is prepared for an attack and, during the raid, it is not unknown for young conscripts to be killed. The government of the Soviet Union is not answerable for deaths in realistic exercises, even in peacetime. The troops on exercise are members of the Spetsnaz, the world's largest special

forces organisation.

Spetsnaz (Spetsalnaya Naznacheniya), the Soviets' special purpose troops, come under the direction of the GRU and consist of 16 Spetsnaz brigades, four Spetsnaz naval brigades, 41 Independent Spetsnaz companies and the Spetsnaz regiments — the latter being available for senior commanders to use as the situation demands. In peacetime, Spetsnaz number some 30,000 men; in the event of war or crisis those ranks can expand to 150,000.

The way in

All Spetsnaz soldiers are conscript and undertake a minimum of two years' military service, with a further five years in active reserve. Those selected will have been earmarked long before they gather at the conscript collecting centres for their compulsory military service. They will not be new to military life. First, they will have been members of the Young Pioneers (YP). This is roughly equivalent to the Boy Scouts. Many of their activities involve traditional field

Scoped AK-74
Photographed in Afghanistan last summer, this AK-74 is fitted with a scope: not normal practice in the Soviet army, but airborne and Spetsnaz troops do receive some special equipment. Other items found in Afghanistan include silenced pistols and new types of body armour

crafts such as hiking, swimming, camping and map reading. Membership is open to all boys and girls between nine and 14 years old. The end product is a politically prepared individual who has basic military skills. The Young Pioneers are linked to schools and are particularly active in Soviet cities and towns.

At 14, young people can join KOMSOMOL, which trains both physical and mental capabilities in military and political activities, to produce a good communist. A year later the young person can elect to join the DOSAAF, the Voluntary Society for Co-operation with the Army, Air Force and Fleets. This is a para-military organisation of some 15 million members, run by former military personnel and equipped by the Soviet armed forces.

Compulsory school finishes at 16 in the USSR. Those not destined for military careers take up civilian jobs but can remain in the DOSAAF, where they will receive further military training – including shooting, parachuting, scuba diving and outward bound training. This will help them when they are called for their two years' military service.

When they are called up, those who excelled in the DOSAAF are offered places at officer candidate school. Those who don't meet the highest standards, but who do want a military career, are taken into the armed forces as NCO candidates. Anyone going to university must join DOSAAF and continue with military training until they have finished their studies, when

they are required to undertake their two years' service.

The conscript collecting centres take in newcomers twice a year – in the 'winter period' or the 'summer period'. Your birthday dictates which one you attend as you are liable for service immediately after your 18th birthday. Women are not subject to compulsory military service, but are selected through the KOMSOMOL and DOSAAF if they are interested in joining the Armed Forces.

At the centre, the conscript is interviewed and his documents scrutinised. Everything about a person is recorded. How did he do at school? Does he have any special abilities? Was he good at sport? Was he loyal to the communist system? Is he a party member? The all important KOMSOMOL and DOSAAF reports give details of his fitness, military skills and determination.

At the top, the best are selected for the KGB, airborne, missile, and intelligence units. A small number are selected for a unit they have never heard of – the Spetsnaz.

Joining the unit

The young man who leaves the collecting centre will be one of about a hundred others. They will travel to a Spetsnaz fighting unit to join other groups from other centres and begin a brutal training course that lasts several weeks.

The conscript will train for either Army or Navy Spetsnaz. His training unit will be within, but separate from, an airborne or naval infantry regiment. His uniform will depend on the service his Spetsnaz brigade is attached to. Army Spetsnaz wear the pale blue beret and blue and white striped T-shirt of the airborne VDV, while Navy Spetsnaz wear Soviet Naval Infantry uniform, a black beret and blue and white striped T-shirt.

The training cadre is made up of officers, warrant officers (*starshina*), sergeants and corporals, with some

Ending the Prague spring in 1968. The Soviet invasion of Czechoslovakia was spearheaded by special forces troops in civilian clothes who seized Prague airport, allowing these Soviet airborne forces to land unopposed and overrun the capital.

private soldiers for administrative duties. Conscripts are kept away from trained Spetsnaz soldiers.

Over the top

For the conscripts there are no weekends, and their day will begin at 0600 hrs with reveille, followed by strenuous exercises and an inspection before breakfast. Fit, strong, elite soldiers need food, and they are well fed. Training then begins in earnest, with the teaching and honing of military skills, including assault courses where the Soviet obsession with live firing will test the new soldier's mettle. From the very beginning live ammunition is used, and accidents, even fatal ones, are considered acceptable.

Physical training and unarmed combat are high on the agenda. Political indoctrination is also important, for these troops will be inserted deep behind enemy lines to carry out their missions, so reliability is paramount. The day may end at 2300 hrs, depending upon how well the group has performed.

In one test, conscripts undertake a cross-country run of 30 km, with ful kit and weapon and wearing a ga mask, all within a set time. If anyon weakens and removes his mask everyone has to return to the start and begin again.

Those who fail to pass Spetsna training are sent to other units to com plete their military service, knowin nothing of the elite unit they almos joined. At the end of the basic selec tion training course about 20 recruit will be left from the original hundred in each group. The conscript is now Spetsnaz soldier – but still with muc to learn. He is constantly scrutised by officers and senior NCOs.

Officer training

The very best are selected for office training, at a special Spetsnaz facult at the higher airborne comman school at Ryazan. They begin fou years of gruelling training, which wil continuously test them. Those who d not make the grade will be re-assigne to airborne VDV units or the ai assault troops.

Those who complete the trainin are aware that they are in an elit organisation. (It is only among officer that the word 'Spetsnaz' is used. Leadership and loyalty are th characteristics of these officers, wh will lead equally hardened mer against well-defended targets withir NATO and further afield, with little o no support from their own militar command.

Other recruits who have done wel are sent to be trained as sergeants. Th six-month course is equally demand ing and many candidates will be sen back to their unit as privates.

Conscripts not selected for officer o NCO training join sections and pla toons of operational Spetsnaz and like their colleagues destined for com mand, will continue to learn the skill of special forces.

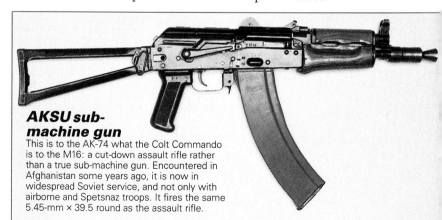

AKSU sub-machine gun

This is to the AK-74 what the Colt Commando is to the M16: a cut-down assault rifle rather than a true sub-machine gun. Encountered in Afghanistan some years ago, it is now in widespread Soviet service, and not only with airborne and Spetsnaz troops. It fires the same 5.45-mm × 39.5 round as the assault rifle.

Combat Report
Mozambique:
Rhodesian Raid on ZANLA Base

Frank Terrell, who served with the Rhodesian Light Infantry, describes a helicopter assault on a ZANLA base in Mozambique.

A sudden decline in terrorist activity was deemed an appropriate time to strike at ZANLA in his own territory. Our Commando was given the task of doing just that in a clandestine cross-border operation – the preliminary to several massive raids during subsequent months.

The night before our departure, we gathered for a briefing in the large bar at Buffalo Range airfield. Intelligence reports suggested that ZANLA had constructed a large military complex deep inside the Mozambique bush. The Security Forces had deliberately given it a wide berth and, as expected, the result was an influx of ZANLA personnel massing for a crossing into Rhodesia.

Among those seen at the camp had been two members of the ZANLA hierarchy, identifiable by their distinctive camouflage uniforms with hammer-and-sickle collar insignia. It was probable that there were also East European military advisers' staying at the base.

The attack begins

Our mission was to capture at least one high-ranking official and anything else of intelligence value. We were also expected to salvage as much equipment as possible and to destroy the rest. Simultaneous to our assault, a Stop Group would be busy laying an experimental landmine along the camp's approach road. Immediately prior to our attack the Air Force was to carry out a precision bombing raid, with the ground troops deploying as the last jet aircraft were unloading their bombs.

The attack commenced on schedule the following morning. Two big Cheetahs and eight Alouette G-Car helicopters were used to transport our assault force of 50 or so heavily-armed troops.

My first glimpse of the ZANLA camp was from about 30 metres above ground level as our Cheetah hurtled towards a distant smoke- and dust-filled skyline, against which could be seen tiny, wheeling specks that were our Hunter and Canberra aircraft. With the scene framed in the Plexiglas windscreen of the helicopter it was almost like watching a movie, with the sound track obliterated by the heavy whump-whump-whump of the spinning rotors.

We flew straight through a pillar of dark smoke, banking sharply around an anti-aircraft gun, amazingly still pumping rounds skywards, then down over a clump of trees, lower still until suddenly the chopper was dropping almost vertically and we were leaping out into the tall yellow grass that fringed the camp. A moment later the helicopters lifted up and headed west, back to Rhodesia.

Bubbling cauldrons

Our 12 sticks lost no time in linking up, whereupon we began to edge our way forward. Initially progress was hampered by the flames that were devouring trees and bushes all round. The pop-pop of discarded small-arms ammunition, detonated by the intense heat, added to the confusion. Elsewhere could be heard the distant sound of sporadic shooting.

My initial view of the camp after deplaning came when we reached a field kitchen set up beneath the shaded cover of a group of trees. Evidence of the speed of our assault was provided by three or four bodies sprawled round huge, bubbling cauldrons of sudsa – the

staple diet of Africa. I picked up an SKS rifle, slung it across my back, and continued with the sweep. While still on the outskirts we shot a number of guerrillas, most of whom were dazed and disoriented by the preliminary bombing.

Gradually we secured the perimeter area and at last moved into the main camp. This consisted of a neatly-organised system of bunkers, weapon-pits and tents. It was all superbly constructed with strongpoints expertly positioned so as to provide the best possible fields of fire. The deep bunkers had been shored with timber, and sandbags surrounded weapon-pits in which were found four AA guns, their barrels still aimed skywards. Behind one of the guns sat a dead terr, probably the same chap who had fired at us as we came in to land. He was now shoved to one side as our men quickly dismantled the heavy weapons while the rest of us continued towards the heart of the base.

Clearing the trench system

This turned out to be an elaborate trench system. There was only one way to find out if the enemy had remained in position, and so began a nervewracking operation oddly out of place in modern warfare. The trenches had been dug in a zigzag pattern with fortified bunkers sited every few yards, so we had to negotiate each section separately, dealing with the bunkers one at a time, using grenades to blast the bunkers before venturing inside. The area was soon cleared, resulting in a vast pile of small-arms and miscellaneous equipment. Amazingly, ZANLA had decided not to stand and fight, choosing to abandon this excellent defensive position before we arrived!

We found many weapons; AK and SKS rifles lay in the red dust or propped in bushes, the barrels aimed in the direction we had just come from. Bulky backpacks were found full of clothing and personal effects. Medical supplies, including ampoules of precious morphine, had been left behind. Nearby were tents filled with camouflage uniforms or stacked high with cases of tinned food – the latter kindly provided by the Red Cross! Discarded water bottles, belts, webbing, bush hats, even steel helmets were scattered everywhere.

Loading the Cheetahs

The Cheetahs were called in and loaded with innumerable rifles, grenades and ammunition. With considerable difficulty we dragged to the LZ a 12.7-mm and three 14.5-mm AA guns. What we could not take was destroyed. The tents were set on fire while the food supplies were scattered and then contaminated with white phosphorus grenades. Thousands of copies of Zimbabwe News – ZANU's official organ – were discovered and used to help fuel the fires.

By mid-afternoon we had arrived at the outer limits of the camp's defences, where we paused for a short rest. Our CO, supervising the operation from the K-Car circling high above, now gave the order to stop moving forward and return to the LZ.

Priceless information

It was at this time that I noticed a floppy bush hat poking up from a thicket a short distance ahead. I yelled a warning to those close to the spot and fired several shots into and just below the hat before running over to examine my kill. There was nobody there, just a perforated hat on top of a battered briefcase! By now a little group had gathered. Carefully peeking inside the case, we saw that it was filled with a stack of

One of the Rhodesian Light Infantry manned heavy machine-gun posts surrounding the Chipinda Pools administration base where the assault force operated from.

typescript. Close examination revealed that it was a list of hundreds of active terrorists and included such priceless information as their bush-names and individual weapon types complete with serial numbers. There were also handwritten messages for delivery, personal letters and a unique collection of photographs depicting uniformed ZANLA personnel posing alongside their Communist instructors.

By last light the assault force was safely back in Rhodesia, where we heard that the minelaying party had a run-in with a number of terrs attempting to escape the main assault force. Some troopers swore that they had seen a white man amongst those lucky enough to escape into the bush!

A successful operation

During a debrief some days later we learned that the operation had been a success. Although we had been unable to bring back any prisoners, we did succeed in providing sufficient information to keep Special Branch busy for weeks to come. Furthermore, the landmines worked a treat. At least one had detonated beneath a fully-laden truck – part of a FRELIMO convoy sent to recapture the camp. Twenty-eight terrorists had been counted as killed, and an array of valuable arms and equipment had been recovered without a single casualty to the attack force.

Waiting for the choppers after the successful conclusion of our raid into Mozambique. The Cheetah helicopters were Bell Model 212s with the doors removed.

WEAPONS OF THE 'WOLF'

THE RUSSIAN SPECIAL FORCES

The unofficial badge of the Spetsnaz is the 'wolf', for wolves hunt in packs and defeat prey much larger than themselves. Spetsnaz too operate in small groups, seeking out the enemy, gathering intelligence and then, when ordered to move, killing or destroying a much larger target.

The ability to do this comes from months of training and exercises, where the men are pushed to their limits. Parachute training will have covered the use of the RS-1 parachute, which has a reasonably slow descent that allows it to be steered. Once skilled in basic parachuting, they move on to advanced training with a military version of the high-performance competition parachute, the UT15. This requires a high level of competence and is used to deliver troops in HALO (high altitude low opening) operations.

Because Spetsnaz may need to operate anywhere in the world and in any terrain or climate, they are regularly parachuted into the northern USSR to survive and operate in Arctic conditions, and into deserts and mountain regions too.

Tools for the job

On the ground the Spetsnaz soldier is equipped with either an AKS-74 rifle or an AKSU sub machine-gun. Snipers carry the SVD sniper rifle. Every soldier carries the P6 pistol for close-quarter work. Grenades and additional ammunition for machine-guns as well as SA-7 SAMs and RPG-7 or RPG-18 anti-tank missiles are issued as appropriate. A knife and the non-folding spade are standard issue. The latter doubles as a hand-to-hand combat weapon. Hours of martial arts training teach the soldier to swing, slice, stab and parry with it, so that it becomes lethal in his hands.

Apart from the anti-aircraft and anti-tank missiles, neither heavy weapons nor vehicles are used, unless the group captures them from the enemy. Support may come from aircraft in the form of ground strikes or

The Spetsnaz have been very active in Afghanistan. Together with airborne units, they specialised in ambushing Mujahideen supply columns like this. They are also closely associated with irregular tribal units paid to fight the guerrillas in their own way.

helicopter gunships or, for naval Spetsnaz, gunfire from warships. Radios are carried to maintain contact with headquarters and to intercept enemy radio nets. Signallers carry portable direction finders to help locate enemy transmissions. Those fluent in the language being listened to may be able to identify a target suitable for attack.

During an exercise in the far eastern military district, the attacking force drew up a plan to attack both the HQ and an important missile unit belonging to the 5th Army. Spetsnaz troops were parachuted in to attack but the defenders, aware of the possible use of special forces, directed motorised infantry to find them. Some of the Spetsnaz came up against a canny adversary. The commander of a missile regiment ordered his vehicles to be positioned around the perimeter, pointing outwards at an angle. The trap was set. When, in dead of night, the Spetsnaz attacked, all of the vehicles' lights were switched on at the same time, leaving the raiders illuminated and exposed in open ground, unable to see their target. The defending commander then ordered the guard dogs loose!

Living rough

Soldiers of the Spetsnaz are not accustomed to luxuries such as central heating and the trappings of

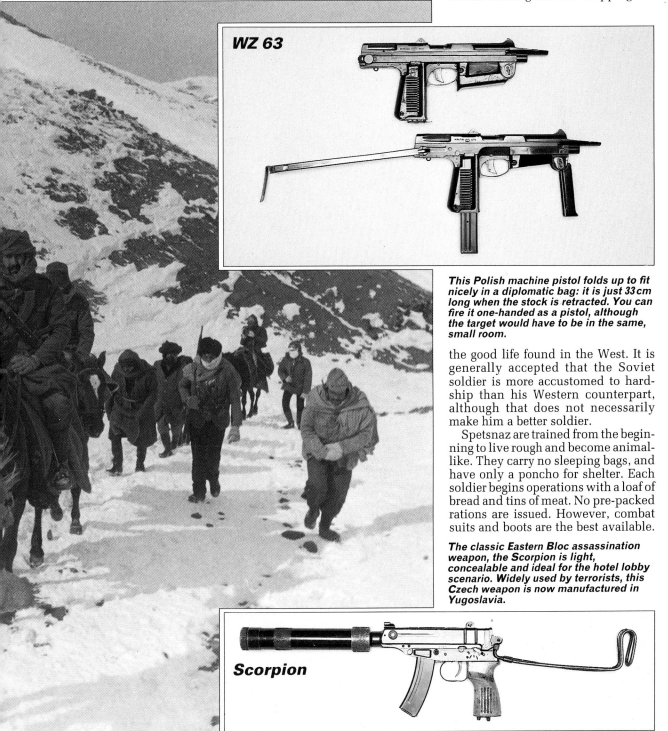

WZ 63

This Polish machine pistol folds up to fit nicely in a diplomatic bag: it is just 33 cm long when the stock is retracted. You can fire it one-handed as a pistol, although the target would have to be in the same, small room.

the good life found in the West. It is generally accepted that the Soviet soldier is more accustomed to hardship than his Western counterpart, although that does not necessarily make him a better soldier.

Spetsnaz are trained from the beginning to live rough and become animal-like. They carry no sleeping bags, and have only a poncho for shelter. Each soldier begins operations with a loaf of bread and tins of meat. No pre-packed rations are issued. However, combat suits and boots are the best available.

The classic Eastern Bloc assassination weapon, the Scorpion is light, concealable and ideal for the hotel lobby scenario. Widely used by terrorists, this Czech weapon is now manufactured in Yugoslavia.

Scorpion

underwater swimming and navigation exercises. Parachute training i
undertaken with descents into water
combined with the techniques fo
operating from submerged sub
marines. Mini-submarines hav
become a key element within Spets
naz. They carry swimmers close to th
target area, allowing teams to 'loc
out' and swim ashore to undertak
reconnaissance, strike political tar
gets, attack military bases or pave th
way for a Soviet naval infantry land
ing.

Each of the four Soviet fleets has a
Spetsnaz brigade, totalling som
5,200 men. Naval Spetsnaz can be
taken overseas by merchant or mili
tary shipping to make reconnaissanc
of possible enemy ports, docks anc
harbours. Naval Spetsnaz undergo the
same military combat training as thei
colleagues in the army brigades, anc
use their amphibious training anc
equipment as a mode of transport
offering greater flexibility than those
on land.

Spare clothes, socks, mess tins,
spoon, wire saw, additional camou-
flaged jacket and a survival kit are all
stowed into the haversack.

Ammunition, grenades and explosives are carried in volume as resupply behind the lines may not be possible, and troops will have to use
captured enemy weapons and ammunition if the situation demands. Each
man carries a water bottle and sterilis-
ing tablets, along with a knife, spade
and pistol. Once the soldiers have
used their food, they have to obtain it
in their operational area, either from
Soviet/Spetsnaz agents or by living off
the land.

Survival training requires troops to
be dropped in remote areas with no
food and the option only to survive or
die. Spetsnaz expect to operate
behind enemy lines – for example in
West Germany or Scandinavia – wearing the uniforms and carrying the
weapons of that country. Army Spetsnaz will undertake deep penetration
of enemy lines, attacking ammunition
dumps, support bases, headquarters
and fuel stores. Disruption and intelligence gathering are priorities.

Join the Navy

Naval Spetsnaz consist mostly of
combat swimmers, supported by
mini-submarines and specialist parachute troops. Based among Soviet
naval infantry, each brigade has
approximately 1,300 men (and an
unknown number of women), making
the Soviet Navy's Spetsnaz by far the
largest amphibious special force in the
world. Within the overall Spetsnaz
organisation the naval brigades are far
more active than their army counter-
parts.

*Spetsnaz are trained to operate in all
climatic conditions. Spetsnaz patrols
fulfil the functions of specialist recce,
which in the British army would not
necessarily be a special forces task.*

Spetsnaz mini-subs and combat
swimmers have penetrated Swedish
territorial waters and have been
observed in the waters both around
the islands and on the mainland, close
to defence bases.

Scuba diving in the Soviet Union
began in earnest in 1956. As the sport
became popular, special centres were
established to cater for greater numbers. During the time spent with
KOMOSOL and DOSAAF, those who
show promise are encouraged to develop their diving skills. By the time
they are selected for Spetsnaz, they
are considered to be master athletes.

At the Soviet naval infantry diving
centre, the Spetsnaz diver/swimmers
learn to use closed-circuit underwater
breathing apparatus on long-distance

On the outside

Spetsnaz soldiers get higher pay
longer leaves and quicker promotior
than ordinary troops. When they com
plete their two years' conscriptior
they have three options. If he ha
proved himself officer material b
exemplary service, a Spetsnaz soldie
may be offered a place at the officers
airborne school at Ryazan. An NCO o
private soldier who doesn't have th
qualities to make an officer can elect tc
become a regular soldier and make th
Spetsnaz a career. He may choose tc
leave, and will then be expected tc
undertake five years' active reserve
Soldiers who stay undertake furthe
specialist courses including lan
guages, advanced explosives and sig
nals, and may find themselve
assigned to an anti-VIP company.

*Spetsnaz are usually equipped with
pistols in addition to whatever else they
are carrying. The 9-mm Makarov is a
surprisingly well-made pistol, which
shoots handles and functions like the
Walther PP.*

*The 5.45-mm PSM is now issued to
police and security units, and its
diminutive size makes it the choice for
concealed carry. The 5.45 × 18 bottleneck
cartridge leaves something to be desired
as far as ballistic performance is
concerned.*

Combat Report

Falkland Islands: Mount Longdon

A former member of 3 Para describes his experiences during the early stages of the campaign to recapture the Falkland Islands.

We were absolutely shattered. All of us had trench foot and each step was like walking on glass. Two days before, we had led the battalion advance on Teal Island, and while the rifle companies had secured their objective our four-man patrol had set up an OP about three miles away to give early warning of any enemy counter-attack.

That night was one of the worst, with a very strong wind, snow, sleet and fog. The temperature was well below freezing. Sleep was impossible, and as the visibility was down to a few metres the four of us lay huddled under a poncho. Then, thank God, on one of our hourly radio checks company HQ told us to get back to Teal Inlet.

We staggered back and spent the night in a barn. The rest of Patrol Company was there and we were only disturbed once in four hours, by an officer wanting us to do stag duties for the rifle companies. The conversation was not a long one but the officer went away shouting threats of court martials. He should have been grateful that we let him live.

A cold night in the open

The following day was spent getting our kit ready for another night move, this time to secure Estancia House. After our first hot meal in four days, we led the battalion to the bridge, north of Lower Malo House, left them there and continued south east to Estancia. Occasionally one of the patrols went off in a different direction to carry out various tasks.

When night fell those of us that were left went to ground about a mile from Estancia, and a patrol went forward to do a CTR (Close Target Recce) on Estancia House itself. The remaining three cleared the surrounding area. The Estancia patrol returned and said that the Argies had left hours earlier.

We prepared to move up to the house but were told we had to wait on orders from Company HQ. We were still there when daylight came, and it was so cold that the worst cases of trench foot had their feet under their oppos' armpits. The order to move forward to Estancia House was eventually given and, not in the best of moods, we set off. When we arrived, we found out that Company HQ had spent the night there.

Now thoroughly pissed off, we retired to a sheep shed and dreamt of revenge. That night the battalion came through our position and moved on to the high ground surrounding Estancia House: 'A' Company was on Mount Estancia itself, 'B' Company on the southern shoulders of Mount Vernet, and 'C' Company on the top of Mount Vernet. We made ourselves at home in the sheep shed and set off on patrols, OPs and CTRs from there.

Shelling the food tent

It was now our task to try to find the minefields around Mount Longdon and to estimate the enemy's strength on the mountain. Many days were spent about a thousand metres from Longdon, as well hidden as possible, noting the number of enemy, where they had dug their trenches, any artillery pieces visible, and anything useful.

My own patrol spent a week 800 metres from Longdon behind a rocky outcrop. We lived on chocolate for the entire time, didn't have any shelter at all, couldn't smoke, and all talking was kept to a minimum. We had to use plastic bags as toilets.

We soon noticed that each day the enemy gathered outside what we took to be the food tent, at exactly the same time: about 50 men in all. On the third day we were ready for them, and radioed our calculations through to the artillery.

Seven seconds later there was a low whistle over our heads and the first round embedded itself in Mount Longdon with a dull thud. It was two hundred metres to the left of the scoff tent. We sent the corrections to the artillery and sat back to watch the fun.

The reaction of the enemy was surprising. Instead of diving for cover like we would have done, they were standing around looking at the shell holes and pointing. Some had even wandered over to have a better look. This soon stopped when more shells whistled over and began to stonk the whole area. Two minutes later the shelling stopped and the smoke slowly cleared. There was no scoff tent and no hungry Argentines.

Pucaras

The survivors started to emerge after five minutes, and collected their dead. We told the artillery our estimate of the dead and wounded – ten dead, fifteen wounded.

We gave another fire mission the following day on to the very top of Mount Longdon, where the enemy commanders were having a briefing. The casualties this time were fewer, but probably a lot more important.

Towards the end of our patrol we had the shock of our lives when two Argentine Pucara aircraft flew over our position at a height of 15 metres and headed for 'B' Company position. We were able to give a warning, and when the Pucaras arrived the lads were ready for them and put up so much tracer and normal fire I almost felt sorry for the pilots. Some joker also fired a Milan rocket at them. The Pucaras didn't hang around, and headed back the way they had come. This time they were even lower over our position, but thankfully they didn't see it.

The enemy hits back

On the seventh night, we retreated from our OP and rendezvoused with another patrol who were taking our place.

Returning down the valley to 'A' Company's position, the peat bog to our left started to explode. It took us about five seconds to realise that we had been spotted and were being mortared. We ran as quickly as possible on the boggy ground and the mortar shells chased us all down the valley. Luckily the enemy patrol must have been inexperienced, otherwise some

A member of 3 Para perched on a rock at a captured enemy position on Mount Longdon.

decent fire corrections on the mortars would have had us.

We reached 'A' Company's position just before dawn and there was the usual struggle to convince the sentry we were really Patrol Company and not a bunch of Argies. When we reached Estancia House and our sheep shed, the patrols there were in high spirits because we had finally been allowed to have a go at the Argies. Snipers had started to do their thing, and one of the teams had even followed up by hitting the enemy with a 66-mm rocket.

That night, news of Patrol Company's first big contact reached us. Two patrols had been doing an OP on Murrell Bridge, close to Longdon. They spotted a group of Argentines who walked onto the bridge and started to mine the surrounding area. As our lads were really close to the bridge detection was imminent, so they decided to strike first.

Hitting the bridge with everything they had – Gimpies, SLRs and grenades – they quickly cleared it, but were then engaged by the enemy from some high ground towards Longdon. The Argentines were using a .50-cal Browning and their fully automatic FNs. After a brief fire fight, the enemy not surprisingly started to get the upper hand and the lads withdrew. They had no casualties, but had to leave all the equipment and Bergens behind. They reached the sheep shed the following day and we had a few beers that one of the reporters had give us. Patrol Company had at last opened their scoring.

Some of the Argentines seemed quite glad to be taken prisoner. This group was captured during the attack on Mount Longdon.

Fighting Fit

IN ACTION

THE RUSSIAN SPECIAL FORCES

The Spetsnaz have been well blooded in Afghanistan. From the numbers of them reported in action, it seems that they have been rotated to ensure that most special force soldiers will have seen active service at some stage. It is difficult to distinguish Spetsnaz from Airborne troops in Afghanistan, but Mujahideen reports do identify Spetsnaz from their numbers and from the fact that they operate by local command decisions rather than by waiting for higher authority to give orders.

In a conventional war, Spetsnaz teams would be small, but, when a large or special target was singled out a number of teams would combine. In Afghanistan, operational teams are about 50 strong and well armed. For instance, a Spetsnaz group of about 50 was reported to have moved through the mountains at night, guided by "loyalist" Afghan militiamen who had lived in the area, to set up an ambush. They established themselves in some disused buildings, in a village reported to be giving aid to the Mujahideen. The Afghan guerrillas entered the deserted village to collect food and the ambush was sprung.

The fire fight was devastating but short lived, the Spetsnaz breaking off contact and withdrawing before assistance could arrive. Three guerrillas were killed and three wounded.

On the other foot

The Spetsnaz have not always had it all their own way. When a team of 24 Spetsnaz soldiers was caught in an ambush laid by the Mujahideen, the ensuing battle lasted all day. Outnumbered, and fighting a determined enemy force, all 24 died. With so many of their élite forces lost, the Soviets retaliated by bombing the closest village, which housed only civilians.

Left: Spetsnaz mountain training is critically important in Afghanistan, where the Special Forces may be called upon to fight some heavy rearguard actions as the Soviet forces withdraw. The British withdrawal from there in 1842 ended in the massacre of a whole army.

Spetsnaz have used helicopters to travel close to contact areas, as the mountain terrain is accessible only on foot. Hind helicopter gunships serve two purposes: they can deposit teams in the mountains, then act as gunships providing support. However, since the guerrillas have obtained Stinger anti-aircraft missiles, the Soviets are loth to use helicopters at close quarters, having lost a considerable number.

In action, Spetsnaz have proved themselves to be hard and well-trained troops, and are the only ones that the Mujahideen have encountered who think for themselves. They have also been known to kill their own wounded rather than let them fall into the hands of the enemy. But this has been a common practice among opponents of the Pathans for many years — the fate of captured wounded was usually beyond description.

Helping hands

Spetsnaz were also in action on 24 December 1968, when a Soviet transport aircraft contacted Czechoslovakia's Prague airport with a request to make an emergency landing. Permission was granted. At the airport, Spetsnaz and KGB personnel dressed in civilian clothes were already waiting as the aircraft drew to a halt. Well-equipped Spetsnaz troops poured from it to join up with those on the ground. The airport was secured, and the signal was given that paved the way for a massive airlift of Soviet troops and equipment. While some Spetsnaz remained at the airport,

Many of the recruits chosen for special forces training will have already gained some experience parachuting with the Soviet youth organisation DOSAAF.

The Soviets have invested heavily in naval infantry and naval special forces. They now lead the world in the deployment of large and powerful hovercraft which can land substantial numbers of troops and exploit their terrific speeds to achieve surprise.

Fighting Fit

others commandeered transport and drove to the Soviet Embassy, then on to the government offices to arrest Czech leaders.

A similar operation occurred in Kabul, capital of Afghanistan, in 1979. Over a number of days, Spetsnaz soldiers in civilian clothes arrived on regular Aeroflot flights, and on 25 December two Antonov transport aircraft landed at Kabul airport and disgorged Spetsnaz troops, dressed in Afghan Army uniforms. They linked up with those who had arrived over the previous days. Once the airport was secure, they moved to the Palace of President Hafizullah Amin, with direct orders: kill the President and everyone in the Palace. With Amin dead, the Soviets' puppet President, Babrak Karmal, was installed. The Spetsnaz re-grouped to be given lists of senior military and political figures who, if they showed any opposition, were to be executed.

In both Czechoslovakia and Afghanistan the first Spetsnaz units on the ground were from the "anti-VIP" companies, whose ruthless, systematic murder showed them to be a formidable force. Follow-up units were from army Spetsnaz, who took the war to the Mujahideen in the mountains.

Elite of the élite

Entry to the "anti-VIP" companies is for those soldiers who decide to

Soviet Special Forces will probably be dropped in small units to seize significant terrain features or attack key NATO targets at the beginning of an East/West conflict. You need have little fear of a mass air drop: it is the platoon from the single Antonov that poses the most serious threat.

The Afghan Mujahideen tend to use the term Spetsnaz more to describe a type of Soviet tactics than specifically identified units. Once these crack troops have been withdrawn, the days of the Afghan communist regime will be numbered.

remain in the Spetsnaz after their two years of conscription. They undergo additional training, with languages a priority. These units can be expected to make use of enemy uniforms and weapons and, in many cases, especially in the preparatory phase before a formal declaration of war, they will operate wearing civilian clothes.

It is in the "anti-VIP" units that women appear to have found a position. They are reported to have been active at Greenham Common, where they were gathering information on the movement of cruise missiles and the defences of the base. In war, Spetsnaz would be required to plant signal beacons or attack such targets.

The Soviet Union also sponsors many of the world's terrorist campaigns and small bush wars by providing weapons, intelligence and training teams. Foreigners are trained at centres in, for example, Libya, Cuba,

It is known that some Spetsnaz train to fight behind the lines, disguised as NATO troops. Other Warsaw Pact nations follow suit: the East Germans even have some M48 tanks, captured in Vietnam, which they maintain in West German colours.

Angola and PLO camps. Spetsna train instructors who gain the 'Spurs' in either the Soviet Union Eastern Europe at foreigners' trainir centres. They then return to their ow country and train the forces involve in a conflict. Cuba and Libya are use as the major centres for both trainin weapon and equipment handling, that a finger cannot be pointe directly at the Soviet Union.

Spetsnaz training teams have esta lished cadres in Southern Afric Central America, Cuba, Libya, Vie nam and Afghanistan. Reports ind cate that Libya was the base for a nav Spetsnaz combat swimmer trainir centre that was bombed during the L air strike against that country. With many terrorist and subversive grou planning actions or carrying them ou the Spetsnaz have a busy future eve without the immediate prospect action on the battlefield.